SPUDFIT

A WHOLE FOOD, POTATO—BASED GUIDE TO EATING AND LIVING

ANDREW TAYLOR

& MANDY VAN ZANEN

Praise for Andrew's first book:

The DIY Spud Fit Challenge:
a how-to guide to tackling food addiction with the humble spud

☆☆☆☆☆ **Inspiring!**
October 24, 2016
Format: Kindle Edition   Verified Purchase

I cannot recommend this book more. Andrew and his wife Mandy have put together a nice, strait forward, encouraging book for anyone battling food addiction or jump starting weight-loss. The science is solid, he has many reputable Doctors support. His research is also on point. Cannot thank him enough for starting his youtube channel and growing his media presence. Watching his recent trip to LA was so inspiring. Thanks Andrew

☆☆☆☆☆ **Who knew the power of the humble potato!!!**
January 11, 2017
Format: Kindle Edition   Verified Purchase

I have learned so much from Andrew's journey to better health. In this book, he addresses in a clear and humorous way, his challenges and successes. The recipes are also super simple and helpful. Who knew the power of potatoes!!! Well done, Andrew!

☆☆☆☆☆ **Easy and Effective**
October 12, 2017
Format: Paperback   Verified Purchase

It's a short, easy to read book. No fluff; to the point. The "behavior modification" that I have tried with other diet programs has not worked. Spud Fit however, offers simple techniques for adjusting one's mind-set regarding food and it seems to be working for me. I've never been on a diet this... easy. I am less stressed on this diet than any other one I've tried (Weight Watchers, Diet Center, 4-Hour Body, and more). I'm 18 days into the potato diet and so far I've lost 6 pounds and I feel pretty good. Not bad for an inactive woman of 50.

☆☆☆☆☆ **Amazing**
December 27, 2018
Format: Paperback   Verified Purchase

I love potatoes, so I decided to try this diet. I have never been able to follow a diet long enough to actually lose any real weight. In the 2 months that I have been following this diet plan, I have lost 32 lbs so far. I am more than pleased. I'm never hungry and this has been the easiest diet I have ever tried. My doctor was a little concerned in the beginning but he is very happy with my blood work and my blood pressure. I would recommend this diet to anyone who likes potatoes. You have to really be a potato lover to do this diet.

Visit *www.spudfit.com* to learn more.

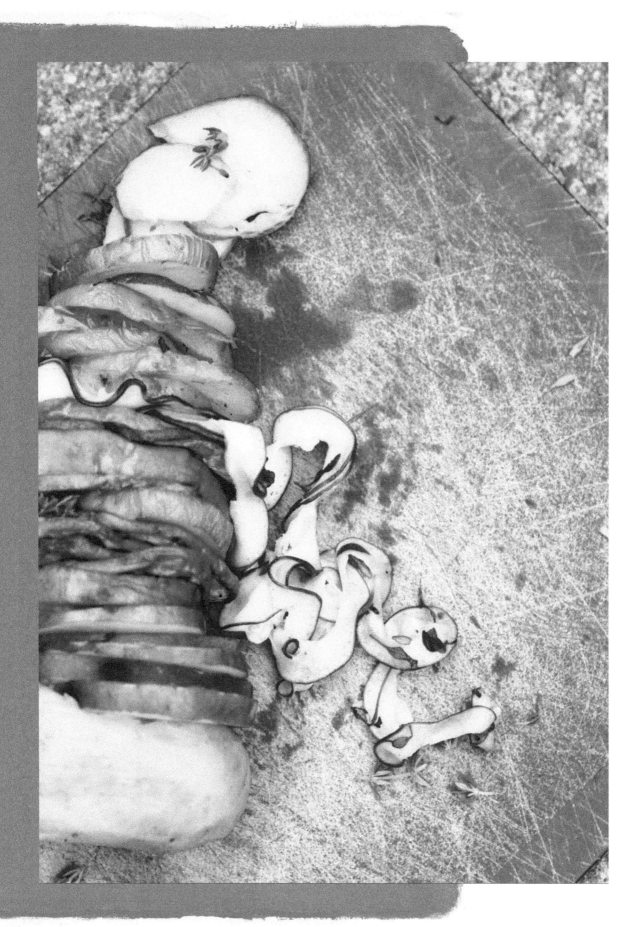

WHERE IT ALL BEGAN

DESPERATE TIMES CALL FOR DESPERATE MEASURES

In November 2015 I was at the lowest point in my life. I was suffering deeply from clinical depression and anxiety. I was crying every day but I couldn't figure out why because I felt totally devoid of emotion. I didn't feel sad, I felt empty and hopeless and I didn't see a reason to cry but it happened every day regardless. I'd reached the end of yet another 'successful' weight loss attempt that had come to a grinding halt with the mother of all binges. It's fair to say I was at my lowest point with no light at the end of the tunnel.

Then I had a moment of clarity when I realised that all my life I'd been trying to lose weight by merely treating the symptoms rather than the causes of my weight gain. I was an excellent dieter - I'd lost weight on every diet under the sun. I'd shed a few kilograms on Atkins, paleo, raw fruit, soup, juice fasting, meal plans, calorie counting, weighing food, chewing 100 times per mouthful and any other diet you care to name. I could white knuckle my way through a month on any diet out there and pat myself on the back for losing 10 kilos along the way. Of course these many successes called for many celebrations too!

On this particular evening in November I decided to reward my great success with a slice of pizza. 'I deserve a slice of pizza to reward myself for such a great month!' I told myself. 'One slice of pizza won't hurt, I can go back to my diet tomorrow.' Of course pizzas aren't delivered by the slice and it's a waste of money to get a small one when the family-sized pizzas only cost a little bit more.

The pizza came, I grabbed a slice and sat on the couch to watch a movie. That slice was the greatest thing to have happened in a month! I enjoyed every bite and before long it was down the hatch. I settled in to the movie, content with my wise decision to only eat one slice and leave the rest of the pizza in the kitchen, out of sight - but not out of mind. After half an hour I thought to myself, 'two slices of pizza in a month isn't much, I'll get up extra early and work it off in the morning and then get back to my diet.' Soon after that I told myself that I'd better get rid of the pizza so it can't cause any more trouble. Of course I couldn't throw it in the bin and waste all that food - there are starving children in Africa after all! The very predictable end to my night involved finishing off the entire family-sized pizza followed by ice cream and soft drink with a side of self loathing and despair.

Of course I didn't get up early and work it off in the morning, nor did I have my green smoothie for breakfast or my salad for lunch. I spent the day wallowing in self pity, lamenting the fact that I always did this. Why couldn't I stick with any diet I tried? Why couldn't I lose weight and keep it off? Why did success always end with

a binge? Why couldn't I just eat junk foods in moderation like everyone else? As I sat on the couch and cracked open a beer, it suddenly hit me like a ton of bricks: I was a food addict! All my life I'd been treating food the way an alcoholic would treat the beer in my hand. We all know stories of alcoholics who can go a period of time without touching a drop of alcohol until a special occasion of some sort arrives. 'Just one beer,' they tell themselves, 'I'll go back to being sober tomorrow'. Of course one beer quickly becomes ten and full blown alcoholism rears its ugly head. My behaviour with food was no different; I was a food addict!

At first this made me more depressed. An alcoholic can quit alcohol, a drug addict can quit drugs, a gambling addict can quit gambling. But what can a food addict do? In my warped state of mind I found myself wishing that I had a drug or alcohol addiction. I knew those would be terrible afflictions and would be hard to quit, but at least the solution was relatively straightforward, if not easy: do not drink alcohol. I started wondering if there was a way to quit food. How close could I get to actually quitting food while still being healthy? Was there a single food that could keep me healthy while I quit everything else?

Six weeks of exhaustive research ensued. I read scientific literature, watched lectures, read books, watched documentaries and devoured anything nutrition related that I could get my hands on. If I wanted to get as close as possible to quitting food and attempt to treat my addiction with the abstinence model, then the choice quickly became obvious: potatoes!

While researching the efficacy of a potato only diet, I also did a lot of soul-searching in an attempt to understand why things had gone so far wrong for me. Why couldn't I do this mythical thing called 'moderation'? I took a deep and honest look at my life and realised how food had been a dominant force in it. I relied on food for comfort, enjoyment and emotional support in every aspect of my life. A bad day at work, relationship troubles, car troubles – you name the problem and I would attempt to make it better with food. On the flip side, I would celebrate the end of the work week with pizza, make a good movie even better with chocolate and chips and somehow improve on the company of friends with massive burgers and desserts. Birthdays, funerals, sporting events, weddings, catch ups with friends, meetings, just watching the TV at home...it seemed like no matter what I did, I somehow used food to try to improve it.

We are commonly told that food should be one of life's great pleasures. We are constantly bombarded with TV cooking shows, food magazines and cookbooks. Celebrity chefs, restaurants and fast food chains are everywhere, like drug dealers on every corner and the straights in between, ready to supply us with the hit we so desperately need. Because food is one of life's great pleasures.

Except when it isn't.

We as a society don't seem willing or able to acknowledge that food can indeed be the cause of some of life's great sadnesses too. I realised that while all this food did provide instant gratification to help me feel better in the moment I was eating, it was actually the root cause of so much misery in my life. The happiness I derived from the taste of food only ever lasted for a fleeting moment, while the weight gain, ill-health and sadness that it caused had the potential to last a lifetime.

The most important thing for early humans was to get enough energy to survive to see the next day. As a result we evolved to get great pleasure from the foods that provided the most calories. Foods that are highest in fat and simple sugars are especially good at triggering the pleasure centres in our brains. If prehistoric people found a doughnut tree they would've gorged on doughnuts until there were none left. Then they would've remembered exactly where it was and maybe even learned to cultivate it so that next time the doughnut tree was in season they'd be able to get even more. The extra layer of fat gained from eating doughnuts would've helped them to survive the winter or get through a drought. Doughnut trees, with all their highly concentrated fats and sugars, would've been super helpful to us for the one month a year that they were bearing 'fruit', and our instinct to seek out these calorie bombs would've served us very well. Of course these days there are doughnut trees everywhere you look, and they're always in season.

This natural instinct to seek pleasure through calorie-dense foods no longer serves us. Seeking out pleasure from food usually ends up doing more harm than good. We've flipped the script on evolution to the point where people who have the most highly developed ability to go against this instinct are more likely to live longer, happier, healthier lives. If using food as a source of pleasure is now causing more problems in society than it solves, perhaps it's worth considering our options. Could we forego pleasurable foods for a period of time and learn to get comfort, enjoyment and emotional support from other areas of life? We need that occasional dopamine hit in our brain, we need to light up the pleasure centres from time to time, but does that have to come from food? Rather than using food for pleasure, could we use it as fuel for our alternative pleasure-seeking efforts?

In order to find out the answers to these questions for myself, I went on a year-long, potato-only diet that became known as 'The Spud Fit Challenge'. An entire year of only potatoes seemed like just about the hardest and most boring thing a person could do, so I knew it was something I needed to try!

The first two weeks were torture, but once I fully embraced the idea of making my food boring and my life interesting, a whole new world opened up to me. My focus shifted away from food and towards finding joy in the simple things in life. I noticed the colours and smells of flowers when I walked past them - maybe that sounds overly hippy, but it's true. I stopped and soaked in the sun for a few minutes on a summer's day. I danced, played and wrestled with my son and I connected more deeply with my wife. I started exercising again - not to lose weight but because I developed a deep desire to get outside and move. I wrote and made videos and connected with people around the world. I shared what I was learning and experienced pure joy when I received emails from people who had been helped by my message. I went from struggling through each day, existing on the boundaries of life, to really being open to the full range of human emotions for the first time in years. Food had numbed my experience of life and 'removing it' had opened up a whole new world. It turned out that for me, the truly great pleasures in life were only unlocked once I stopped looking for pleasure in food.

TRUST THE PROCESS
LET THE NUMBERS TAKE CARE OF THEMSELVES

My weight was only ever a symptom of a bigger problem: my relationship with food. I had always focused on treating the symptom, without ever dealing with the cause. This time I wanted to make the cause my absolute focus, so I intentionally set no weight loss goal. If so much of the negativity in my life came from seeking comfort, enjoyment and emotional support from food, then it made sense to me that I should set up a situation where that would not be possible. If I forced myself to eat only a food that would not and could not satisfy my needs for comfort, enjoyment and emotional support, then I'd have no choice but to learn new ways of attaining those things. I'd have to find more healthy ways to get the dopamine hits that are so valuable (and enjoyable) in life.

My only goal was to go a year eating only potatoes and whatever happened outside of that goal would just be something interesting to take note of. My approach would be entirely process-driven: focus on my actions - eating only potatoes - and let the numbers take care of themselves. When an alcoholic quits drinking they don't have any weight loss or fitness goals - all that's important is that they don't drink alcohol. I wanted my Spud Fit Challenge to have that same level of simplicity. Success would be very simple to measure: if I stuck to only potatoes for the day then that was a success. Trying to somehow improve on that was pointless.

CALORIE DENSITY
HOW TO EAT MORE AND LOSE WEIGHT

'Eat less, move more' is commonly understood as the be-all and end-all of weight loss. If you want to lose weight then you should consume fewer calories while also burning more. Pretty simple really. This book focuses on the 'eat less' part of that statement, but not in the way most people would think.

'Eat less' is synonymous with hunger, deprivation and misery and, for most of us, can only be maintained for a finite period until we run out of willpower and it all becomes too much. When we try to 'eat less' we are ultimately fighting a losing battle - it never ends well!

There is a better way. We can eat fewer calories while actually eating a bigger volume of food by focusing on the calorie density of what we eat. We can literally eat as much as we want of veggies and fruits and still lose weight. You read that correctly: if you eat this way, you can eat as much as you want without putting on weight! In a full-blown potato binge you'd struggle to get 1000 calories, whereas a pizza and ice cream binge could easily hit 5000 calories. If we concentrate on eating whole, unprocessed veggies, fruits, beans and grains then we can eat to our heart's content in the knowledge that, despite our full stomachs, we are actually eating less!

Calorie density refers to the number of calories per bite or weight of food.

(Note: I discuss this in calories and pounds simply because most of the research comes out of the U.S, and also you're more likely to eat a pound of food than a kilogram! For reference, there are roughly four kilojoules in a calorie, and two pounds in a kilogram).

- Non starchy veggies contain around 100 calories per pound.

- Fruit contains around 300 calories per pound

- Potatoes, corn, pumpkin and oats around 400 calories per pound

- Rice, pasta and other whole grains around 500 calories per pound

- Beans and other legumes around 600 calories per pound.

After this we start to get into dangerous territory for those of us who are trying to lose weight. Any food that is over 600 calories per pound is likely to trigger the pleasure centres in our brain, releasing a rush of dopamine to give us the deliciously dangerous 'high' that we crave. This sort of physiological response to calorically dense food is best avoided because not only is the food itself high in calories, it also keeps us coming back for more and more, setting us on a cycle that is difficult to break.

Nuts, seeds, avocado and coconut are health-promoting foods, but are best avoided by those of us who are trying to lose weight as they are calorically very dense, and very easy to over-consume. Meat, dairy and eggs are also higher in calorie density while providing no fibre. Processed grains and flours (white ones, not wholemeal) have been stripped of their fibre content and valuable micronutrients, making them a more concentrated source of calories than their whole, unprocessed counterparts. Processed sugars hit 1800 calories per pound. At the top of the calorie density chart is oil (of all kinds - even olive oil and coconut) at around 4000 calories per pound!

On that note, there are many people, including many of those who have contributed to this book, who don't have and who have never had weight problems and who don't suffer from food addiction. Nuts, seeds, avocado and coconut are higher in calories and are featured in some of the recipes. If you are trying to lose weight then it's best if you leave these ingredients out. Trust me, you'll be fine without them! There are a couple of 'cheese' sauces in the book: if you are trying to lose weight then substitute one that has cashews for one that doesn't. A couple of recipes contain a cup of nuts. This might seem like a lot, but when it's spread out over four serves then it's a relatively small amount of nuts per serve (unless you can't stop yourself from eating the whole lot). No matter your goals, if you want to have coconut yoghurt or coconut milk (neither of which are whole, unprocessed foods), make sure it's a low fat variety with no added oils. Better still make it yourself!

There are some recipes that include bread and pasta. I have no problem with this as long as it is truly wholemeal - check the ingredients to make sure there's no processed white flour before you buy it. Wholemeal breads and pastas contain all the fibre of the original grain which makes them low in calorie density and health promoting.

The most important thing about a healthy diet is that we can stick to it, day in and day out, for the long term. Dr John McDougall (see page 19) has talked extensively about how important it is to make healthy food palatable so that we're happy to stick with it as a staple in the long term. Table sugar isn't ideal but if a teaspoon sprinkled over your oats in the morning means you'll eat oats instead of eggs, bacon and pancakes, then go

for it. Similarly, there are healthier choices than BBQ sauce that contain a little added sugar, but if a small squeeze of sauce means you're happy eating potatoes for dinner rather than a huge cheesy pizza followed by cake, then I say add the sauce! This was the exact rationale behind my choice to add a little flavour to my potatoes for my year-long challenge. I didn't think it would be possible to eat literally nothing but potatoes for the whole year, but if I allowed myself some flavour then there was a glimmer of hope that it could be done.

In the end we all have to figure out what our own triggers and limits are. Some people can eat a small handful of nuts and then stop, while I won't stop until they are all gone! I can eat one or two slices of wholemeal bread with soup while others would easily eat the whole loaf. It's up to you as an individual to be honest with yourself about the type of foods that are likely to spark a binge and send you on a downward spiral.

THE RULES

WHEN QUITTING ALCOHOL, YOU HAVE ONLY ONE RULE: DON'T DRINK ALCOHOL! 'QUITTING FOOD', AS I WAS ATTEMPTING TO DO, WOULDN'T BE QUITE SO SIMPLE, BUT I DID THINK IT WAS IMPORTANT TO HAVE RULES AND THAT THEY BE AS CLOSE AS POSSIBLE TO THAT SINGLE RULE FOR ALCOHOLICS. SO I CAME UP WITH A FEW RULES TO GUIDE ME THROUGH:

RULE NUMBER ONE: GET MEDICAL SUPERVISION.

This was my wife's rule actually. I was a typical Aussie bloke in this way – I'd done my research and was confident in what I was doing, so I didn't think it was necessary to get anyone else to supervise and confirm what I already knew! My wife is usually a little more cautious and thoughtful than me and when she offered her full support of my idea, with just this one condition, I knew she was right. Of course when making any drastic dietary change it is important to do it with help from a medical expert who can keep a trained eye on things for you.

RULE NUMBER TWO: EAT AS MUCH AS YOU FEEL LIKE, WHENEVER YOU FEEL LIKE IT.

This was definitely not an attempt at weight loss and I didn't want it to become one. I didn't want to fall into the same old trap of trying to lose weight faster by eating less and less until eventually my hunger got the better of me and I did something stupid. I'd failed with that approach hundreds of times before and I didn't want to allow myself the chance to travel down that same tired old road. We make our worst decisions when we are hungry, so I figured that if I wanted to stop making bad decisions then I should stop allowing myself to go hungry! I had potatoes with me at all times – usually double what I thought I would need – so that I could be sure that I'd always have enough to eat and that the hunger excuse couldn't be used. It's also important to note that the rule itself contains no mention of the word hunger. I did that on purpose because I wanted this to be as simple as possible; there was no need to try to think about whether I was hungry enough to eat or if I was experiencing the 'right type of hunger' (whatever that means!). If I felt like eating for any reason at all, I would eat. Our instincts have been honed over millions of years for a reason and I didn't want to fight them any more.

RULE NUMBER THREE: EAT POTATOES! USE MINIMAL HERBS, SPICES AND SAUCES.

This rule came about out of fear, I guess. I really didn't think I had it in me to do a whole year on only plain potatoes, so I decided to allow some flavouring to make it a little easier. As long as the condiments contained no oils, nuts, avocado, coconut, animal products or anything else high in fat, then I could use them sparingly. Nearly all of my meals were plain mashed, boiled or baked potatoes with nothing on them, but occasionally I would allow myself some flavour to help me through. One teaspoon of sauce on a large baked potato was enough to change the flavour a little when I just couldn't face another plain, boiled potato!

That's it! Three golden rules for my Spud Fit Challenge – everything that couldn't be covered by these three rules was just noise and not worth putting any time and energy into.

I've modified my rules somewhat since my Spud Fit Challenge finished. At the end of that year I was wary of throwing out all the rules and going crazy with eating everything under the sun. A set of strict rules with a very narrow focus had served me well, and I was aware that I could consider myself to be a 'recovering addict' of sorts, so I wanted to continue with the same sort of outlook. I still keep my focus narrow, just not quite as narrow as I did. The first two rules remain the same but I have a new Rule Number Three - eat as much fruit, veggies, grains and legumes as I want, with a focus on potatoes, using high fat healthy foods such as nuts, seeds and avocados only sparingly. I was fully aware of the danger of suddenly removing all boundaries and creating a free-for-all situation that could turn ugly very quickly. My Spud Fit Challenge is a never ending process, just like any other addiction. There is always room for improvement and growth. I can always get fitter, stronger and healthier.

EQUIPMENT SUGGESTIONS

By now you know my philosophy and you know that you don't need any fancy equipment at all to eat potatoes. However, there is nothing wrong with having some fun in the kitchen and finding new and different ways to enjoy potatoes - again, if that's what helps you to stick with this way of eating, then do it!

The following is a list of appliances and items we've found to be particularly useful for helping to cook old favourites without the bad bits:

NON-STICK FRYING PAN. Very high quality for water/stock or dry frying. We like granite (stone). Ceramic is also good. You tend to get what you pay for, so if you have limited funds, do your research and direct them here.

AIR FRYER. Buying an extra large air fryer has changed our lives - chips without the oil is the stuff dreams are made of (see Morgan Mitchell's recipe on page 89)! Contrary to manufacturers' instructions, you don't need any oil at all. Use an air fryer not just for potatoes but for a whole range of vegetables, tofu/tempeh - anything that you want to be crunchy without the side effects of deep frying. An air-fryer is basically a small oven without the pre-heating time and clean up.

FOOD PROCESSOR/BLENDER. We keep it pretty simple on a daily basis, but now and then we cook for family and friends and want to get large quantities chopped or grated quickly, or we want to blend soups, or make home-made sauces, dips or dressings that we know are super healthy. A food processor with all the bells and whistles is great for this, and a heavy-duty commercial blender is great for making light work of hard items and large quantities with ease. But you can easily get by with a hand-held stick/immersion blender for most purposes - and these have the added benefit of easy clean-up.

PRESSURE COOKER OR SLOW COOKER. They are sort of the opposite (one cooks fast and one cooks - wait for it...slowly!) but the effect is the same: a one pot meal. We cook at least one full pot of plain potatoes every day to use in all sorts of meals, but these also make it so easy to make a healthy soup, stew or casserole with minimal effort: put everything in, set it to go, and simply wait.

WAFFLE IRON. So many times people have asked me 'but what do you eat for breakfast?'. The simple answer (potatoes) is apparently not very interesting, so sometimes I say 'potato waffles', and sometimes that's true! Place a whole medium boiled potato in each waffle segment, close the waffle iron as far as you can, wait - for a long time - and eventually you're left with a whole food, crunchy delight. It couldn't be easier to breakfast like a king.

SPECIAL INGREDIENTS

NUTRITIONAL YEAST

You will see nutritional yeast pop up in quite a few of these recipes, and with good reason.

Referred to as 'nooch' by the cool kids, nutritional yeast is a strain of deactivated yeast (meaning that it can no longer ferment) that imparts a strong cheesy, nutty or umami flavour. It comes as a flakes or a powder, and can be used in sauces, dips, vegan Parmesan, cheesy mash, to top popcorn - wherever savoury 'cheesy-ness' is desired.

Nooch is actually a complete protein - one serving of two tablespoons contains 9 grams including all nine of the amino acids that aren't produced by the body! Even unfortified it is a source of iron and several of the B vitamins, and fortified it provides an easy and delicious way to get the all-important B12.

Nutritional yeast is available in health food shops and many supermarkets and is known by several different names (most commonly savoury yeast flakes) - but don't mistake it for brewer's or baker's yeast!

LIQUID AMINOS SEASONING

Liquid aminos are exactly what they sound like - liquid amino acids. They're a great substitute for soy sauce, providing an earthy, rich, savoury flavour without the wheat or fermentation, so they're especially handy for anyone who is avoiding gluten or alcohol.

Of course if you like soy sauce and have no problem with gluten or fermented products then you can feel free to substitute these substitutes for soy sauce! Aminos are available mainly in health food stores, or buy it online.

THE FORKS ♟♟♟

The forks denote the level of effort required to make each recipe. Recipes with few ingredients and few steps in the method have been allocated few forks, and vice versa.

FOOD OF THE PEOPLE
AND PEOPLE OF THE FOOD

Leonardo da Vinci said 'simplicity is the ultimate sophistication', and I couldn't agree more. This book as a whole is mostly an exercise in simplicity, a nod to minimalism. We need a total rethink of our ideas around food and the way we should eat. Potatoes (and all foods for that matter) are edible at all times of the day and night - do we really have to eat cereal only in the morning and potatoes only at night? Many of the meals in this book would traditionally be seen by the mainstream as sides, or otherwise incomplete, for no other reason than they don't contain a huge slab of meat. We don't need to buy into the traditional mainstream, we can fill our plate with sides and make a huge, delicious, health-promoting meal if we choose!

This 'Whole Food Spud Based' way of life is about learning to enjoy food again, but this time enjoying the right kinds of food. In fact these days I enjoy my food more than ever because I know that it's doing me good while my far more refined palate detects subtle flavours in everything I eat. Learning to embrace natural flavours and appreciate the foods I eat gives me so much more than just sensory pleasure. Food can be one of life's great pleasures, without the down side. When we eat whole, unprocessed plant foods we get the best of both worlds. We can have our (potato) cake and eat it too!

Putting this book together has been a very exciting experience for me. I've loved seeing how all of these incredible people approach the food that fuels them and I'm excited by the multitude of flavours and culinary traditions explored from all over the world. Potatoes absorb whatever flavours you want to throw at them and I've discovered that pretty much every corner of the planet has a traditional potato dish!

Since my Spud Fit Challenge I've discovered a huge plant-based movement, full of people who are changing the world in all sorts of ways. I've got to know a whole heap of amazing people and made some incredible new friends, all of whom share my love of potatoes! In this book you'll find contributions from chefs, doctors, researchers, psychologists, athletes, dieticians, nutritionists, naturopaths, health advocates, activists and people with incredible personal stories. All of these people live very different lives and food plays a different role for each of them. Some of them love to spend time in the kitchen creating masterpieces while others keep things very minimal.

One thing they all have in common is that they are fiercely passionate about the power that plants hold to change our personal health and the health of the world around us. Potatoes are traditionally a much-maligned food, thought of as just empty carbs. The amazing people in this book and the recipes they've contributed will show you just what a powerhouse potatoes actually are - a food unique in its ability to not only sustain good health but also taste great, fill you up and provide comfort at the same time. Potatoes, more than any other food, truly are the complete package in more ways than one. Now is the time for them to reclaim the crown as the rightful king of the food world.

Spud up!

SPUD FIT

My wife Mandy has always loved going out to restaurants and trying new things. A big part of the reason she loves travelling is the experience of immersing herself in a new culture, and food is always a huge part of that. Having young kids has curtailed the restaurants and travel to a large degree, but it hasn't dampened Mandy's curiosity and love of food and the experiences that come with it. Food allows her to experiment with other corners of the world and experience the textures and flavours that are so deeply rooted in history and tradition. Our change to plant-based eating has only enhanced the experience, allowing Mandy more scope to experiment with different techniques and to find new ways to create healthy versions of the dishes she's discovered. Necessity is the mother of invention and, for Mandy, taking a handful of ingredients out of the equation has only broadened her creativity. After all, there are way more herbs, spices and plant foods available to us than there are animal foods, so why not find out what they can all do?

MANDY VAN ZANEN

Mandy can make anyone believe with all their heart that not only are their wildest dreams possible, they are within reach. She can talk to anyone about anything; people feel instantly at ease and comfortable baring their soul to her. Telemarketers hang up the phone having sold nothing and gained a whole new perspective on life! Mandy is by far the most passionate, excitable person I've ever met and she'll go to the ends of the earth for anyone who is willing to work as hard as she does. She loves nothing more than seeing people push their boundaries and expand their horizons.

Mandy has always been a foodie but has never considered herself to be any kind of cook until she got roped into all this by me! You'll see that she's pretty awesome in the kitchen, but her true creative talent lies in music - she has a music degree in classical singing from the Melbourne Conservatorium, and not only does she sing all sorts of pop music, she also plays the drums, orchestral percussion and the clarinet as well! It's only in recent years that she's really found her niche as a musician: reimagining her first love - classical art music - as contemporary popular songs.

Mandy is my dream woman and the most incredible mum our boys could hope for. She shows them how to live, how to laugh and how to love. She'll walk through fire for her boys in a heartbeat. She's the yin to my yang. We are

totally different people in so many ways but we are the same in all the ways that matter. They say behind every successful man is a woman. I don't like that saying - we stand together.

'STAMPPOT' [MASH POT]
BOERENKOOL, GEROOKTE WORTELS,
APPELMOES EN NOOTMUSKAAT

The Dutch were not only eating mash before Andrew, they were also eating kale (kool) waaay before it was cool. Growing up with a Dutch dad, we ate this ultra-traditional dish (it dates from at least 1574!) a couple of times a week, followed by vla (custard) for dessert. The mash itself comes in many variations, including with cabbage (or it's pickled counterpart, sauerkraut), endive, spinach or some other kind of leafy green like kale. It's usually served with rookworst (smoked sausage), but I use carrots instead, which give you the smoky taste and a bit of texture, but without all the nasty bits. It's the ultimate comfort food, served with another Dutch staple: appelmoes (apple sauce) and a sprinkling of nutmeg. Eet smakelijk!

Serves 2

4 medium whole carrots, boiled or steamed
1 tablespoon ready-made apple sauce, to serve (preferably low or no sugar)
pickles, pickled onions or gherkins, to serve
Marinade
1 tablespoon maple syrup
1 tablespoon tamari or soy sauce
1 tablespoon balsamic vinegar
1 teaspoon vegetable stock powder
½ teaspoon onion powder
½ teaspoon garlic powder
1 teaspoon smoked paprika
1 teaspoon French mustard
¼ teaspoon ground black pepper
¼ teaspoon caraway seeds
¼ teaspoon ground coriander
½ teaspoon dried oregano
½ teaspoon dried thyme
¼ teaspoon ground nutmeg, plus extra to serve

Mash
4 medium mashing potatoes
½ onion, roughly chopped
plant-based milk of your choice, for mashing (if needed)
1 teaspoon vegetable stock powder
1 bunch curly kale, finely chopped

For the marinade, combine all the ingredients in an airtight container with 125 ml (4 fl oz/½ cup) water and mix well.

Take the steamed/boiled carrots and roll them around gently in the marinade, making sure they are fully coated. Cover and leave to marinate in the refrigerator for at least 3 hours, preferably overnight. Turn the carrots at least twice while they're marinating.

For the mash, boil or steam the potatoes until tender, about 20–30 minutes.

Put the onion in a frying pan with 60 ml (2 fl oz/¼ cup) water and fry until soft.

Drain and mash the potatoes roughly, then add the milk, stock powder and fried onions. Mix in the raw kale until well combined.

Heat a frying pan over a high heat. Remove the carrots from the marinade and dry-fry until thoroughly heated and just starting to char. You can also grill or barbecue them.

Serve the carrots on top of the big bowl of mash, topped with a tablespoon of apple sauce, a sprinkling of nutmeg and a few pickles on the side.

MOROCCAN TOMATO SOUP
HERBED POTATO DUMPLINGS

I love this recipe because I get excited by strong flavours, and this dish is packed full of them! Note that the dumplings are heavy, in both texture and taste, because they're made with wholemeal flour and are, of course, egg-free. Healthy, exotic and deeply satisfying – what more could you want?! Leave out the tahini if you're trying to lose weight. I recommend making the soup the day before to allow the flavours to mingle.

Serves 2

Soup
1 tablespoon vegetable stock powder
4 garlic cloves, crushed
1 onion, chopped
1 carrot, chopped
1 celery stalk, chopped
1 tablespoon ras-al-hanout (see Note)
1 x 400 g (14 oz) tin chickpeas, drained
2 x 400 g (14 oz) tins crushed tomatoes
1–3 teaspoons lemon zest (depending on how much you like lemon)
2 teaspoons tahini, to serve (optional)
1–3 teaspoons fresh chopped herbs, to garnish
lemon wedges, to serve
Dumplings
2 medium baked potatoes, cooled (see Note)
75 g (2¾ oz/½ cup) wholemeal self-raising flour
1 teaspoon each of chopped coriander (cilantro), chives and flat-leaf (Italian) parsley

To make the soup, combine the vegetable stock powder with 250 ml (8½ fl oz/1 cup) water in a saucepan. Add all the remaining ingredients, except the crushed tomatoes and lemon zest, and bring to the boil over a high heat. Cook until the vegetables have softened.

Add the lemon zest and continue cooking for another 30 seconds, then add the tomatoes and mix well. Bring back to the boil, then turn off the heat and cover with a lid. Set aside.

For the dumplings, mash the spuds in a mixing bowl. (They need to be well mashed but not totally smooth.)

Sift in the flour, bit by bit, then knead the mixture with your hands to form a dough. Make sure that the flour is mixed in, but don't overmix. Add more flour if the dough is sticky, and more water – a splash at a time – if it's too dry. Add the fresh herbs and mix again briefly to combine.

Bring another saucepan of water to the boil.

Break off small pieces of the dough and roll into balls (see Note).

Carefully drop the dumplings into the boiling water. Once they rise to the top, cook for 1–2 minutes, then remove them to a plate using a slotted spoon. Continue until all the dough has been used.

Reheat the soup, then divide the soup and dumplings evenly between two bowls. Stir in 1 teaspoon tahini, if using. Garnish with fresh herbs and serve with a lemon wedge on the side.

Note

Baked, cooled potatoes are by far the best option for this recipe. You can cook them however you like, but steamed or boiled potatoes will have a higher water content and will require much more flour when it comes to mixing the dough. It doesn't taste as good and requires more cooking, so I usually bake mine.

Small is better with these wholemeal dumplings; you can make bigger ones and cook them for longer if you like, but they get bumped in the water and tend to break apart.

If you can't find ras-al-hanout, use ½ teaspoon each of paprika, cumin, ginger and coriander instead (all ground).

EASY LOW–FAT MAYONNAISE
by Joel Kirkilis (page 97)

125 ml (4 fl oz/½ cup) aquafaba (see page 98)
½ teaspoon mustard
2 teaspoons apple-cider vinegar
pinch of sea salt

Combine all the ingredients in a blender. Easy!

Note from Mandy

For a creamier (but higher fat) version, add ½ cup
of cashew nuts.

BLT POTATO SANDWICH

Who doesn't love a BLT?! Not me! The potato sandwich needs no explanation, and the tempeh provides the smoky, chewy crunchiness that we know and love. Makes 1

½ quantity of Marinade (page 4)
150 g (5½ oz) tempeh
2 small potatoes, for the 'sandwich'
½ teaspoon vegetable stock powder
½ teaspoon onion powder
½ teaspoon dried parsley

To serve
mashed avocado with a squeeze of lemon to avoid discolouration
thinly sliced tomato
crunchy cos (romaine) or iceberg lettuce leaves (as many as you can handle)
oil-free barbecue sauce
mayonnaise (see page breakout box, left) or garlicky aioli (see page 11) without the tarragon

Put the marinade in a small airtight container.

Cut the tempeh into thin slices (imagine how you'd like them on a sandwich), place in the marinade and gently stir to coat. Cover with a lid and leave to marinate for as long as possible (several hours, or overnight) to develop the flavours.

Grate the potatoes and spread them out on a plate. Microwave on high for 1 minute, or

until they become sticky from the starch.

In a mixing bowl, combine 1 teaspoon of water with the stock and onion powders and dried parsley. Mix well.

Add the potato and stir until well coated. Heat a frying pan or grill to medium heat.

Divide the potato mixture in half and place in the pan, forming two round 'pancakes'. These will become your sandwich. Flatten them a little with a spatula, but try to keep them dense so that the potato sticks to itself. Don't make them too thick either, or they won't crisp properly.

Cook for about 5 minutes, until golden brown on the bottom, then turn them over gently and continue cooking for another 5 minutes on the other side. If you try to turn them too soon, they will fall apart.

Once the potato pancakes have become fairly stiff, remove them from the pan and set aside to cool. When all the moisture from the potatoes has been absorbed, they should slide straight out of the pan. This means they're ready.

To cook the tempeh, you have three options:

1. In the oven – Cook the tempeh for 10–15 minutes at 180°C (350°F), keeping a close eye on it to ensure it doesn't burn.

2. In a non-stick frying pan – Fry the tempeh (no oil) over a medium heat for 5 minutes, then over a high heat for another 1–2 minutes, or until any visible moisture is gone.

3. In an air-fryer (my preference) – Cook the tempeh in an air-fryer at 200°C (400°F) for 5–7 minutes. The slices should come out slightly chewy in the middle and crispy at the edges.

To assemble your sandwich, I prefer this order: sandwich slice, mashed avocado, tempeh, sliced tomato (add some pepper here), lettuce, barbecue sauce and mayonnaise spread inside the top potato sandwich to reach the edges.

SUPPORTING LOVED ONES THROUGH CHANGE

by Andrew

We settle into a groove in our relationships where we have clearly defined roles and responsibilities. We gain an understanding of the way our partner behaves on a day-to-day basis, and how they react in certain situations. We learn how to make them laugh and how to help them when they're down. We figure out the fun things we can do together and we know when to leave each other alone. Our lives become so deeply connected and intertwined that we can feel like much more than a partnership; we become two parts of the same person. The term 'my other half' certainly makes sense to those of us lucky enough to have experienced true love.

Changes in our lives affect far more than just ourselves. Everyone around us will be affected – in one way or another – when we change the way we think and behave, and no one is affected more than our partners. Changing the way you eat doesn't have to change your relationship. The following is a guide to make change easier on your partner.

DON'T EXPECT THEM TO CHANGE TOO. Just because you have decided to embark on a major life change, it doesn't mean that your partner should join you for the ride. If your partner is unhealthy, then they already know it, and your efforts to change will no doubt be prompting them to question if they should do the same. Far from asking, pushing and pleading for them to join you, offer reassurance that your efforts are simply to improve yourself and are strictly about you and you alone; they needn't feel pressured to do it too. The only thing you need from them is their understanding that you are doing something that's important to you.

PRACTICE MAKES PERFECT. Since long before my Spud Fit Challenge, the top shelf of our fridge door was where we kept the chocolate, and it remains that way today. Mandy really loves chocolate, but she's one of those alien types who can eat one square then not touch it again for a week. Rather than pressure Mandy to get rid of the chocolate, I decided to use it as practice. As a P.E. teacher, I know that the only way to get better at throwing a ball is to practice it. I also now think that the only way to get better at beating cravings is to practice doing it. Rather than expecting those around me to maintain a pristinely healthy environment at all times, I chose to view that top shelf of the fridge door as my own personal no-go zone. I knew where Mandy kept the chocolate and before I went near it I would take a couple of seconds to prepare myself, then use it as an opportunity to do my beat-my-cravings 'push-ups'. Every time I opened the fridge without eating the chocolate, I pictured my beat-cravings muscles getting stronger. Two years later, and I still haven't even had the smallest taste, and most of the time I don't even register that it's there.

You don't need to demand that your house is emptied of all temptation. Instead, look for opportunities to exercise your muscles and do it again and again, and again. Eventually, having your partner's chocolate in the house won't be a big deal. In fact, you'll be able to square up to it, stare it in the face, then reach right past it for something nourishing.

Now, I'd like you to hand this book over to your partner, let me talk to them for a minute please!

G'DAY, I'M ANDREW AND I'M HERE TO HELP.

I know this can all seem crazy and ridiculous and like yet another attempt at getting healthy that is destined for failure. I know it can sometimes feel like an inconvenience and even a burden on you and I know you already have enough on your plate. I know it can be hard when people close to you make big changes; it holds a mirror up to you and forces you to have some tough internal conversations. When loved ones get healthy, it naturally puts pressure on us to do the same. It can be scary too: what if we can't go to our favourite restaurant anymore? What if we can't cook our favourite meals? What if it changes who we are? What if our partner wants us to change too? What if they don't love us anymore?

I hear from people all the time that their partners are sabotaging their efforts, either by accident or on purpose. They enable wrong behaviours or encourage past bad habits. But I think this sabotaging is mostly driven by fear – fear that our partners are making positive changes while we're left behind. I know you don't want to be a saboteur, you want to be a model of light, love and encouragement. You want to see your partner become everything they ever wanted to be, and most of all you want them to be happy. So what can you do to make that happen?

It's very simple, the number one thing you can do is... drumroll... absolutely nothing! Just go on living your life and let them do what they need to do, after all, it's not about you. If you'd rather not eat what your partner is having, take it on yourself to prepare your own meals. That's it! Seriously, this is an individual journey that you are not required to take any part in. Just go on living your life and loving your partner. Sit back and watch your caterpillar become a butterfly.

One last bit of advice - if you're feeling stressed, eat a potato!

EASY LOW–FAT GARLIC AIOLI
by Mandy

125 ml (4 fl oz/½ cup) aquafaba (see page 98)
80 g (2¾ oz/½ cup) cashew nuts (soaked overnight in
 water if you don't have a powerful blender)
2–4 roasted garlic cloves (depending on your taste)
½ teaspoon onion powder
1 tablespoon lemon juice
herbs/spices of choice, to taste

Combine all the ingredients except the herbs or
spices in a blender. Blend on low speed until the
cashews are incorporated, then slowly increase
the speed to high. Continue blending on high for
2–3 minutes until the sauce has thickened. Add the
tarragon and blend for another 10–15 seconds. Easy!

GLOBE ARTICHOKES MASH AND GARLICKY TARRAGON AIOLI

I'm sure I'm not the only Francophile here. I used to eat all of those stereotypical French dishes – like steak tartare and garlic snails – with gusto, until I realised that what I was actually enjoying were the flavours they were cooked in and accompanied by. Especially tarragon. I love tarragon. And garlic. Lots of garlic. Mmm...

I also had a close shave with an artichoke at a French restaurant in Rotterdam once – I had no idea how to eat it and I almost choked, so I'm happy to be here to tell the tale! If that sounds like you too, make sure you read the instructions carefully! **Serves 1**

1 bay leaf
1 globe artichoke
1 quantity Dr Barnard's Mash (page 21)
Aioli
(see breakout box, left)
1 teaspoon tarragon (dried or fresh)

Make the aioli, using tarragon as your herb of choice.

Bring a large saucepan of water to the boil and add the bay leaf. Wash the artichoke thoroughly, then chop off the stem and tips and remove the choke.

Carefully place the artichoke in the boiling water (you can also place it in a steamer basket over a saucepan of water if you'd prefer to steam it). Cook for about 30 minutes, turning it now and then to ensure it cooks evenly. The artichoke is ready when the leaves are easy to pull off.

To serve, heat the mash (if cold) and place a dollop in the centre of a plate. Make a small indent in the middle for the artichoke. Sit the artichoke upright in the middle and fan out the leaves for maximum visual effect. Serve the aioli in a small dish on the side for dipping the leaves.

Eat by removing the leaves, one by one, dipping in the aioli and sucking the 'meat' at the bottom of each leaf through gritted teeth. As you reach the end of the leaves, you will find the heart. This is the best, best bit – savour it!

EASY OIL–FREE HUMMUS
by Mandy

2 tins chickpeas, one drained, one with the liquid
1 tablespoon vegetable stock powder
1 teaspoon onion powder
juice of half a lemon (or more, to taste)

Blend until smooth. Easy!

TU–NO MORNAY ON SALT– VINEGAR POTATO WAFFLES

Tuna mornay was so exotic in the culinary wasteland that was 80s suburban Australia and, like most other things about Australia in the 80s, I find it hilarious. So it's only appropriate that, as an 80s child who embraces what we now know about good nutrition, I re-invent this dish in a healthy way with a silly name. The nori sheets give it a hint of the sea, while the chickpeas offer texture.

Serves 2 normal people, or 1 Andrew

1 x 400 g (14 oz) tin chickpeas
1 celery stalk, chopped
½ onion, chopped
1 nori sheet, torn into small pieces
100 g (3½ oz/½ cup) fresh or frozen corn kernels
65 g (2¼ oz/½ cup) fresh or frozen peas
80 g (2¾ oz/½ cup) chopped red capsicum (bell pepper)
2 teaspoons chopped flat-leaf (Italian) parsley, to serve
squeeze of lemon, to serve
freshly ground black pepper, to serve
Waffles
2 medium boiled spuds
splash of white wine vinegar (I prefer white wine vinegar, but any vinegar will work)
pinch of sea salt
Mornay sauce
1 small steamed spud
125 ml (4 fl oz/½ cup) plant-based milk of your choice
½ teaspoon onion powder
1 teaspoon French mustard (or to taste)
½ teaspoon vegetable stock powder
½ tablespoon nutritional yeast (optional)

Start with the waffles, because they take ages.

Heat a non-stick waffle iron to the highest setting. Squash the spuds into the waffle cavities, close the lid and leave to cook for about 20 minutes. If your waffle maker is not heavy duty, you may need to cut them in half to be able to close it far enough.

While the spuds are cooking, prepare the tu-no mornay. Empty the chickpeas and their juice into a non-stick frying pan. Mash with a fork just enough to squash them without turning the mixture to mush.

Add the celery, onion and the nori, set the pan over a medium heat and fry until the vegetables are soft. Add the corn, peas and capsicum, adding a little water as needed to avoid anything sticking. Cook for another 2–3 minutes, just to heat – not cook –the vegetables. Remove from the heat and set aside while you make the sauce.

Place all the sauce ingredients in a food processor and blend until smooth. Taste and adjust the seasoning if necessary.

Carefully lift the lid of the waffle iron to check on the potatoes. If they are not quite done, they will pull apart, so go very slowly. They are done when you can poke a knife under one corner and it lifts away easily. Splash or brush over the vinegar and sprinkle with salt.

Add the mornay sauce to the pan of tu-no mixture and heat through again over a medium–low heat.

Serve the tu-no on the potato waffles and garnish with parsley, a squeeze of lemon and a sprinkling of black pepper.

KATE TAYLOR
ANDREW'S MUM

They say the apple doesn't fall far from the tree and I'm proud to say that in my case it's true. I'm a lot like my mum in many ways - it's just a shame she wasn't able to pass on her cooking genes!

Mum is a passionate and gifted educator who can connect deeply with kids of all backgrounds and abilities. She's fierce in her beliefs and pursuit of equal opportunities for all. She taught me to look at situations from all angles by adopting the opposing point of view to me on a wide range of topics, just to stimulate thought and debate. This was my education in thinking outside the square. It's what ultimately led me to look at my own situation in a way that nobody else had before and come up with my unique solution.

Mum is a poet, a traveller, a learner, an explorer, a comedian and a gifted cook. Mum loves nothing more than a big gathering of all her favourite people around a table that's never quite big enough, despite multiple upgrades over the years! Her Christmas lunches are the stuff of legend, with leftovers to keep the good vibes flowing right into the New Year; one year we counted 27 different veggies, all prepared in their own way! When mum cooks, everyone goes home happy and well-fed.

SPUDS ᴡ ASPARAGUS + EDAMAME

ᵞ ᵞ ᵞ ᵞ ᵞ ᵞ

I was a bit chuffed when Andrew asked me to contribute a recipe to his book. I thought I might do a gnocchi recipe in honour of the gorgeous Teddy Taylor, my grandson, who went for almost a whole year where he would only eat fresh gnocchi with nooch! Some people might think that's a bit extreme, but hey – he is Andrew's son!
Unfortunately I'm not really a gnocchi fan, but I thought I would contribute this adapted recipe instead. I think gnocchi, if you like them, would go well in this dish instead of the potatoes; fry them off after boiling to add a nice bit of caramelisation to the dish. Enjoy!
Serves 4-6

750g (26½ oz) potatoes, peeled and cut into 2cm pieces
2 or 3 cloves garlic, crushed (or more if you love it!)
500g (17½ oz) fresh asparagus, trimmed and cut into 4cm pieces
200g (7 oz) fresh or frozen edamame (without pods)
¼ cup of lemon juice
1 teaspoon of grated lemon zest
¼ cup chopped parsley
½ cup nutritional yeast

Preheat the oven to 180°C (356°F).

Place the potatoes on a tray lined with baking paper and bake for 20-25 minutes.

Add the garlic and mix, distributing it evenly among the potatoes. Return to the oven for another 20-25 minutes or until the potatoes are golden brown. While the potatoes are baking, make the topping.

In a large pan on medium high heat, fry the asparagus in a tablespoon of water for two minutes. Transfer to a large bowl and set aside.

Add the edamame to the pan with 2 tablespoons of water and fry, stirring occasionally, until tender (approximately 3 minutes). Drain and add the edamame to the asparagus.

Once the potatoes are cooked, add to the asparagus and edamame and stir through the lemon juice, zest, parsley and nutritional yeast. Serve topped with extra nutritional yeast if you like!

DOCTORS

The whole food, plant-based movement is rapidly expanding across the globe, supported by an amazing bunch of doctors who understand the importance of lifestyle. Doctors are the first port of call for health-related matters, placing them on the frontline in the fight against obesity, diabetes, heart disease, cancer and other chronic diseases. This chapter features these courageous professionals, who are willing to buck convention and tradition by endorsing a different approach to nutrition. Not only do they understand the importance of diet, but they have seen first-hand the incredible impact that a whole food, plant-based way of eating has on a wide range of illnesses.

Perhaps more than any other group, doctors truly understand the power of plants - and especially potatoes - in preventing and reversing some of the biggest killers we have. A whole food, plant-based diet is the only treatment of any kind that has ever been shown to not only slow but actually reverse heart disease. It has also been shown to effectively treat a whole host of other chronic diseases, such as diabetes and arthritis – even some forms of cancer have been shown to respond well. Not to mention obesity, which is a direct contributor to many of these diseases.

Across the length and breadth of the available scientific literature, we see overwhelming evidence that eating more plants leads to better health outcomes. In practice, we consistently see that the healthiest and longest-lived people on the planet get the highest proportion of their calories from plant-based foods that are rich in starchy carbohydrates. Read on to see how the people who are bridging the gap between the science and its application like to eat their spuds, and how it's similar to my approach in its simplicity: nothing fancy, just wholesome, sound nutrition that happens to be delicious and satisfying.

DR JOHN MCDOUGALL

Without Dr John McDougall, this whole crazy 'Spud Fit' experience would probably never have happened, I'd probably be another 20 kg (44 lb) heavier than I was, more depressed than ever, and with a major health catastrophe on the horizon.

When I first wondered about the possibility of living on one particular food while quitting everything else, I did what everybody does and consulted Google. The first thing that came up was a YouTube video, entitled 'Potatoes, the Perfect Food' (put this book down right now and go and watch it!). Without knowing it, Dr McDougall was in the right place at the right time to fan the spark and turn it into a roaring flame. He led me down the rabbit hole of research (which devoured six weeks of my life) to eventually conclude what he'd already known for decades: potatoes really are the perfect food.

Dr McDougall is a true hero of mine and one of the godfathers of the plant-based movement. He's hard-nosed and relentless in his pursuit of the truth and his efforts to share it with the rest of us. He's passionate about his

message and has a depth of knowledge that is unparalleled in the world of health as far as I can tell. Most importantly he's kind, caring and compassionate, and he's been there for me from the beginning. When I was approached by 'The Doctors' TV show in the US, my first thought was that they would do their best to make a fool of me. I wasn't interested in that. I told them, 'yes I'll come on the show, but only if you get Dr McDougall on the show at the same time'. My jaw dropped to the floor when they emailed back that he'd agreed!

A physician and nutrition expert who teaches better health through vegetarian cuisine, Dr McDougall has been studying, writing and speaking out about the effects of nutrition on disease for over 50 years. Dr John and Mary McDougall believe that people should look and feel great for a lifetime. Unfortunately, many people unknowingly compromise their health through poor dietary habits. Other than my wife, nobody has done more for me in this whole experience than Dr McDougall, and I get the feeling that there are countless others who would say the same.

CROCK POT PIZZA POTATOES

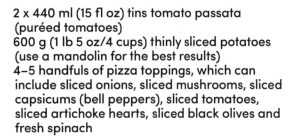

I saw this recipe on our bulletin board a couple of months ago and it sounded so interesting that I had to try it. We have made it several times in the past few months and enjoyed it very much. It is very easy to make and cook, as you can put it in the Crock-pot (slow cooker) and forget about it until it's time to eat. Serves 6–8

2 x 440 ml (15 fl oz) tins tomato passata (puréed tomatoes)
600 g (1 lb 5 oz/4 cups) thinly sliced potatoes (use a mandolin for the best results)
4–5 handfuls of pizza toppings, which can include sliced onions, sliced mushrooms, sliced capsicums (bell peppers), sliced tomatoes, sliced artichoke hearts, sliced black olives and fresh spinach

Mix 60 ml (2 fl oz/¼ cup) water into the passata and set aside.

Place half of the sliced potato in the bottom of a Crock-pot (slow cooker) and top with your choice of pizza toppings. Pour over half the tomato sauce. Add the remaining sliced potatoes in another layer and finish with the remaining sauce. Cover and cook on low for 6–8 hours.

DR NEAL BARNARD

As a food addict, I was initially drawn to Dr Barnard's work because he acknowledged the addictive nature of junk foods. He even wrote a book called 'The Cheese Trap', which is all about how dairy triggers certain reactions in our brains to make us keep coming back for more.

Dr Barnard is another of those who I consider to be one of the godfathers of plant-based nutrition and health. He has authored many groundbreaking studies, including some fascinating and impactful work on type-2 diabetes. He is president of the Physicians Committee for Responsible Medicine, and has made a great contribution to the acceptance of plant-based diets in the dietary guidelines for Americans.

It's not all about food though; one of the best talks I've been lucky enough to hear was Dr Barnard's presentation on how music can affect health. Oh, and he's an amazing guitarist too! Is there anything he can't do?

CHEESY CANNELLINI & ROASTED GARLIC WHIPPED POTATOES

Everyone loves mashed potatoes, and this is one of my favourite ways to make them. Combining roasted garlic, cannellini beans and cauliflower with creamy golden potatoes creates a wonderful buttery texture, perfect as a side dish or as a meal in itself. Serves 4–6

3 good mashing potatoes, peeled and cut into medium diced
1 rosemary sprig
1 thyme sprig
1 x 400 g (14 oz) tin cannellini beans, drained and rinsed
1 garlic head, roasted in foil until soft, or 2 tablespoons prepared roasted garlic
125 ml (4 fl oz/½ cup) plain unsweetened soy milk or other non-dairy milk
1 teaspoon sea salt
1 teaspoon freshly ground black pepper
15 g (½ oz/¼ cup) nutritional yeast
1 bunch spring onions (scallions), sliced

Put the potatoes in a large stockpot and cover with cold water. Drop in the rosemary and thyme sprigs. Bring to the boil over a high heat, then reduce the heat to medium–low and simmer until the potatoes are easily pierced with a fork, about 20 minutes. Drain the potatoes and set aside.

Meanwhile, blitz the cannellini beans in a food processor with the roasted garlic. Add the soy milk, salt, pepper and nutritional yeast, and blend until well combined.

Gradually add the diced potatoes, about a cup at a time, to the food processor and process until smooth. Season with extra salt and pepper if needed, then garnish with the spring onions.

WHAT IS FOOD ADDICTION?
by Andrew

Any behaviour that we continue to carry out despite knowing it is doing us harm can be classed as an addiction. Smokers and alcoholics are usually fully aware that their behaviours are harmful but, for a variety of physical and psychological reasons, they continue to smoke and drink. Food addiction is no different. Everyone knows that ice cream is unhealthy, yet many people who are already obese or suffering other ill-effects of a junk-food diet keep on shovelling it in. The first step to improving the way we eat is understanding why we eat certain things. It's often a question of addiction as much, if not more, than anything else.

DR ANTHONY HADJ

When my story first went viral, things got crazy very quickly. It felt like I was doing interviews nonstop with radio and TV shows from all over the world. It was mostly a lot of fun, but one thing I was unprepared for was the backlash from so-called 'experts' in the media who only wanted to criticise me and insist that I was being foolish and dangerous. I was preparing for another interview live on mainstream TV when an email came through from Dr Anthony Hadj. I was expecting more criticism, but was pleasantly surprised to find words of encouragement and reassurance that what I was doing was healthy and safe, and that I should ignore all the doubters and naysayers. Fast forward a couple of years, and I am still good friends with Ants. I'm constantly inspired by his boundless positivity and dedication to helping his patients heal through the power of plants, especially potatoes!

Dr Hadj was inspired to go plant-based by the likes of Doctors John McDougall (see page 19) and Caldwell Esselstyn, and he now incorporates this healthy way of eating into the management plans of his patients both young and old. I've even seen his prescription pads with healthy recipes scribbled out on them! Anthony focuses particularly on the mental health effects of living with a chronic disease, and finds great pleasure in seeing his patients become happier, healthier, lighter and free of medication.

CHEESY HUMMUS POTATO BAKE

Serves 6

8 medium-sized white potatoes
1 onion, sliced
1 teaspoon balsamic vinegar
90 g (3 oz/1 cup) sliced closed cup
 mushrooms
75 g (2¾ oz/½ cup) sundried tomatoes
50 g (1¾ oz/1 cup) baby spinach
30 g (1 oz/½ cup) nutritional yeast (optional)
sea salt and freshly ground black pepper
Cheesy topping
60 g (2 oz/½ cup) diced cauliflower
40 g (1½ oz/¼ cup) diced raw cashew nuts
1 teaspoon onion salt
½ teaspoon ground turmeric
1 tablespoon chopped rosemary leaves
(optional)
Hummus
3 x 400 g (14 oz) tins chickpeas, drained
1 x 400 g (14 oz) tin cannellini beans (these
 have a slightly nuttier taste than other beans)
3 tablespoons hulled tahini
125 ml (4 fl oz/½ cup) lemon juice
3 garlic cloves

Peel and cut the potatoes into 1cm (½ in) slices. Place them in a large saucepan and cover with cold water. Bring to the boil and cook until they are just starting to soften but are still holding their shape. Drain, reserving 500–750 ml (17–25½ fl oz/2–3 cups) of the cooking water.

For the cheesy topping, place the cauliflower and cashew nuts in a bowl and add the onion salt and turmeric. The turmeric will provide some colour as well as bringing a unique flavour to the dish. Add the rosemary leaves, if using.

To prepare the hummus, combine the tinned chickpeas and cannellini beans in a blender. Add the tahini, lemon juice and garlic. Blend to mix, then add enough of the reserved potato cooking water to blend the hummus to a smooth paste.

Heat a frying pan over medium heat and gently sauté the sliced onions in a little water and the balsamic vinegar. The vinegar will add a lovely caramelised sweetness. As the onion softens, add the mushrooms, sundried tomatoes and spinach. Mix well and simmer until reduced slightly.

Add the hummus to the pan with the onions and gradually add 250 ml (8½ fl oz/1 cup) of the potato cooking water to prevent the sauce from thickening too much (it will thicken as it cools).

Stir in the nutritional yeast, if using, then stir over a low heat for another couple of minutes.

Preheat the oven to 180°C (350°F).

Lay the sliced potatoes in the base of a large baking dish, leaving as few gaps as possible. Add a layer of hummus, then continue layering potatoes and hummus until both have been used. Sprinkle a generous amount of the cheesy topping on top. Bake for 20 minutes, switching to the grill setting of your oven for the last 5 minutes to brown the top.

Although you will be very tempted to eat it straight away, try to let it settle for 10 minutes to allow the sauce to thicken. Of course, if you are like me and it's just too delicious to wait, dig in!

When Dr Mondo asked to interview me a while back, I wanted to find out who he was before I said yes. As soon as I read his website and saw that so much of his energy and effort was spent helping people change the way they think about and relate to food, I was sure we'd become friends. I knew from first-hand experience that the way we eat has a profound impact on the way we think, and it was so refreshing to see a genuine expert approaching the problem of health from a similar angle, that is treating it first and foremost as an emotional issue.

Dr Mondo is a licensed psychotherapist, professor and academic researcher specialising in drastic weight loss, health and wellness. He conducted the first research on the psychological implications of weight loss with former contestants of NBC's 'The Biggest Loser'. His research revealed that emotional and psychological support were an often-neglected part of long-term weight loss success.

He is now on a mission to transform the way the medical field supports people during weight loss. His online program, 'Rewriting My Story with Dr Mondo', is quickly becoming a go-to resource for people wanting to address the psychological side of weight loss. In search of more energy and sustainable weight loss, Dr Mondo transitioned to a whole food, plant-based diet in September of 2017. Going plant-based has helped him effortlessly lose weight, gain health and add a new element to his wellness message, which is that eating this way can help us 'rewrite' our story.

LOADED 'CARNITAS' PAPAS

Serves 4

150 g (5½ oz) oyster mushrooms
900 g (2 lb) your favorite potatoes (red, yellow or russet, or even a combination)
2 teaspoons onion powder
2 teaspoons garlic powder
2 teaspoons paprika
2 teaspoons chilli powder
2 teaspoons coconut aminos
Marinade
juice of 1 lemon
juice of 1 orange
juice of 1 lime
2 tablespoons chilli powder
1 tablespoon garlic powder
2 tablespoons hot sauce of your choice
To serve
½ small red cabbage
ready-made, oil-free salsa of your choice
ready-made, oil-free guacamole
15 g (½ oz/¼ cup) coriander (cilantro) leaves

Chop the oyster mushrooms into small pieces and place in a large, resealable bag. Add all the marinade ingredients, seal the bag and shake well to mix. Refrigerate for at least 2 hours to marinate.

Scrub the potatoes in cold water, then cut them into small dice and place in a large mixing bowl. Add the spices and aminos, and mix well.

Heat an air-fryer to 190°C (375°F) and air-fry the potatoes for 25 minutes. Alternatively, heat a conventional oven to 180°C (350°F) and bake the potatoes on a baking tray for 45 minutes to 1 hour.

While the potatoes are cooking, heat a large frying pan over a medium heat. Empty the mushrooms into the pan and fry for 10–15 minutes, turning frequently, until the mushrooms have a crispy crust.

Layer with the potatoes, salsa, guacamole, red cabbage and coriander to serve.

DR GARTH DAVIS

When I first came up with the crazy idea to eat only potatoes for a year, one of the obvious questions I had was "what about protein?!". I read quite a few studies on human protein requirements and looked closely at the amino acid profile of potatoes. But the thing that really put this question to bed was reading Dr Davis's book, 'Proteinaholic'.

It is extremely well researched and referenced, and does a great job of explaining how society has become obsessed with protein. This obsession has led to a huge deterioration in the health of our population as we continue our never-ending search for more and more protein, usually in the form of meat, dairy and eggs, which bring with them a multitude of negative health implications.

This book cemented for me the idea that I didn't actually need as much protein as I had previously thought, and I realised that potatoes could easily meet my needs.

I've since met Dr Davis and heard him speak a couple of times. He's straight down the line, pulls no punches and is happy to take up the fight against nutritional misinformation. He's a bariatric surgeon who deeply cares for the health of his patients, and always encourages lifestyle-based intervention instead of, or in conjunction with, surgery. If all that wasn't enough, he walks the walk with the best of them, having completed several Iron Man Triathlons (he'd comfortably sit alongside the athletes in this book too).

K.I.S.S LOADED SWEET POTATO

Good health doesn't have to be expensive, time consuming or complicated. My favourite recipe is ridiculously simple, easy, cheap, healthy and delicious. **Serves 1**

1 x 400 g (14 oz) tin black beans, drained
2–3 tablespoons pico de gallo (or to taste)
¼ avocado
large handful of chopped baby spinach
1 baked sweet potato
hot sauce, to taste

Pile it all up on a baked sweet potato. That's it! Boring. But effective!

POTATO POPULATIONS
by Andrew

For a long time, the entire population of Ireland lived on a diet that consisted of about 95 per cent potatoes! During this time, they went through a population boom and it was noted that they were physically bigger and more attractive than their English counterparts from across the border. Similarly, the Okinawans have traditionally eaten Japanese sweet potato as the greatest component of their diet, while having the highest number of centenarians in the world. There are Papua New Guinean highlander tribes who – almost exclusively – eat orange sweet potatoes, except on feast days, and these are big, strong, athletic people. Throughout history, populations who embrace potatoes and other whole, unprocessed foods high in carbohydrates have always enjoyed great health and longevity.

DR IRMINNE VAN DYKEN

I first met Dr Van Dyken at the 'Healthy Lifestyle Expo' in L.A, during my 'year of spuds'. As a general and trauma surgeon, she is the last port of call when all else has failed and a part of you needs to be operated on, bypassed or removed entirely.

It was inspiring to listen to her presentation, 'Avoiding the Surgeon's Scalpel', as a surgeon who is actively trying to put herself out of business!

Dr Van Dyken places heavy emphasis on prevention and reversal of disease using diet and lifestyle alone. It is especially rewarding for her to see her patients do a 180-degree turn and completely restructure their lives around plant-based living. In fact, the changes she has seen are unprecedented.

She lives in Maui, Hawaii with her equally inspiring and lovely husband Russell, 15-year-old dog Chaucer and two cats. In her spare time she enjoys yoga, photography, sailing, cycling and playing various musical instruments. She has been vegetarian since she was 9 years old, and strictly plant-based since 2010.

Dr Van Dyken is on the board of the Vegetarian Society of Hawaii and has a passion for educating others and sharing the benefits of healthy plant-based living. She and Russell created 'Out of the Doldrums', a YouTube channel and online presence promoting healthy, active, plant-based living.

RUSSELL'S TURMERIC INFUSED SUPER DUPER ANTIOXIDANT 'CHEESE' SAUCE

We love this 'cheese' sauce because it is a good way to get turmeric into your diet. Turmeric is my favourite medicinal spice. It contains a compound called curcumin, which is loaded with tonnes of health benefits. Not only is curcumin a powerful anti-inflammatory agent, but it is also antibacterial, antifungal, reverses apoptosis (programmed cell death), slows ageing and accelerates wound healing. I have always joked that if I could buy stock in curcumin I would become rich!
This sauce is delicious over baked potatoes, other vegetables, nachos and our favourite, tacos!
A word of caution, though: because this recipe contains nuts, it is not a low-calorie food. If you are trying to lose weight, it's probably best to consume this sauce sparingly.
Makes 125 ml (4 fl oz/1/2 cup)

1 red capsicum (bell pepper), stalk removed
4 tablespoons tamari or soy sauce
40 g (1½ oz/¼ cup) cashew nuts (or other nuts of your choice)
30 g (1 oz/¼ cup) walnuts
juice of 1 large lemon or lime
15 g (½ oz/¼ cup) nutritional yeast
½ tablespoon ground turmeric (or a 5 cm/2 in piece fresh turmeric root, peeled) (see Note)
pinch freshly ground black pepper
1 jalapeño chilli, stalk removed, or 1 tablespoon chilli flakes (optional)

Combine all the ingredients, including the jalapeño (if using), in a high-speed blender and blitz to a smooth purée. Store in an airtight container in the fridge for up to 1 week.

Note

For a spiced variation on this sauce, try replacing the ground turmeric with ½ tablespoon Madras curry powder.

DR JOEL KAHN

Listening to talks and reading articles by Dr Kahn did a lot for my understanding of how diet affects cardiovascular health. He helped to ingrain in me the knowledge that, despite popular opinion, carbohydrates from whole foods do not clog arteries and cause heart attacks. In fact, a diet free from processed foods and animal products does just the opposite. He helped give me confidence that my Spud Fit Challenge would do great things for my heart health – confidence that was backed up by fact as the results of my medical check-ups improved more and more throughout the year.

Dr Kahn is an internationally known cardiologist who has treated thousands of patients during heart attacks. He is a Summa Cum Laude graduate of the University of Michigan School of Medicine, and the first physician in the world to be certified in Metabolic Cardiology. He now treats and prevents heart disease using nutrition and integrative therapies.

He serves as Clinical Professor of Medicine at Wayne State University School of Medicine. He has authored five books - all bestsellers - the latest of which is 'The Plant-Based Solution', and he has been featured on 'Dr Phil' and 'The Doctors' TV shows.

He opened GreenSpace café in Ferndale and Royal Oak, Michigan, where he and his family serve several thousand plant-based meals every week.

LOADED SWEET POTATO GREENS + SPROUTS

I love potatoes because they are delicious, can be found almost anywhere I travel, are great for grabbing on the run, and come in so many varieties. This recipe uses sweet potato; so rich in beta-carotene, which becomes vitamin A in our bodies. It can be made with a white potato or even a large purple potato or yam. How simple is this goodness? Any potato, any bean, any green, any spices, add some sprouts, and you have a meal fit for a healthy king or queen. I love that you do not need oils, and that you can get such a nutrient-dense meal in just minutes. I eat a loaded potato like this for lunch several times a week and I hope you enjoy it as much as I do. **Serves 2**

2 medium sweet potatoes
1 garlic clove, minced
250–500 ml (8½–17 fl oz/1–2 cups) vegetable broth
1 bunch kale, washed, de-stemmed and torn into pieces (or organic baby spinach or rocket/arugula)
1 x 400 g (14 oz) tin black beans, drained and rinsed (or chickpeas or cannellini beans, preferably organic in BPA-free tins)
handful of sprouts, to serve
salsa of your choice, to serve (optional)
sea salt (optional) and freshly ground black pepper, to taste

Preheat the oven to 200°C (400°F).

Pierce the potatoes a few times with a fork and place on a baking tray lined with baking paper. Bake for 1 hour, or until tender and easily pierced with a sharp knife. Set aside to cool slightly.

Heat a small saucepan over a medium heat and sauté the garlic in the vegetable broth.

Add the kale, cover and cook for 2–3 minutes, then add the beans and cook for another couple of minutes. Season to taste with salt and pepper.

Cut the potatoes in half lengthways and top with the beans and greens mixture. Finish with the sprouts and some salsa, if using.

SWEET POTATO & RED LENTIL STEW

This recipe was one of the first plant based recipes that my family all agreed that they liked when we transitioned to a plant based diet. It is simple, cheap, quick and delicious! What is there not to love? Serves 8

4 spring onions (scallions), diced
2 celery stalks, diced
155 g (5½ oz/1 cup) grated carrot
2 litres (70 fl oz/9 cups) vegetable stock
2 cloves garlic, minced
500 g (1 lb 2 oz/2 cups) red lentils
2 large sweet potatoes, peeled and cut into
2.5 cm (1 in) dice
2 tablespoons thyme leaves
sea salt and freshly ground black pepper,
to taste

Place a large stockpot over a medium heat. Add the onions, celery, and carrots with about a 125 ml (4 fl oz/½ cup) vegetable stock and sauté until the vegetables are soft. Add more vegetable stock as needed to keep the vegetables from sticking. Once the vegetables are soft, add the garlic and sauté for 1 minute.

Add the red lentils, sweet potatoes and thyme. Increase the heat to high and bring to the boil, then reduce to a simmer and cook for 20–25 minutes until the potatoes are soft. Season to taste with salt and pepper and enjoy!

DR LAURIE MARBAS

I first met Dr Marbas when she asked me to be a guest on her podcast. She's bright in every sense of the word and shines on everyone around her. Knowledge is power and she has bucket loads of it. She wants nothing more than to share that power with those who need it most. Dr Marbas is not just a great doctor, but a great educator too. She believes that every person has the right to know how to eat to prevent and reverse chronic disease, and she emphasises the inherent simplicity in positive lifestyle changes.

DR LUKE WILSON

I first heard of Dr Luke Wilson when news broke of a big study that he was the co-lead author of. The study involved guiding a group of people through the transition to a McDougall-style whole food, plant-based diet. The research subjects achieved greater weight loss and more improved health than in any previous study where subjects were allowed to eat as much as they wanted. I was especially excited by this, because it backed up rule number two of my Spud Fit Challenge: to eat as much as you feel like, whenever you feel like it.

Dr Luke Wilson is from Wellington, New Zealand. In his final year of medical school, he studied and worked in Santa Rosa, California, as an intern for Dr John McDougall (see page 19) at the McDougall Health and Medical Center, and also alongside Dr Michael Klaper and Dr Alan Goldhamer at the True North Health Center.

Luke founded 'Two Zesty Bananas', a science-based health and wellness website, with colleague Dr Matthew Hobbs in 2014. Since then, he has co-authored 'The 21st Century Food Course', a six-week crash-course for adopting a plant-based lifestyle, completed the T. Colin Campbell Center for Nutrition Studies 'Certificate in Plant-Based Nutrition', worked part-time as a general practitioner and spoken at events in New Zealand and Australia. He has experience helping hundreds of people transform their lives by adopting a whole food, plant-based lifestyle.

SIMPLE PUMPKIN & SWEET POTATO SOUP

Simplicity. It's not the flashiest, but it sure works. Andrew's 'Spud Fit'-approach to his plant-based transition, as well as being a study on the versatility and nutrition of the potato, attests to the power of keeping it simple. When I started out plant-based, I didn't have an amazing cookbook full of recipes to help me make those first steps. So, I started here: this recipe is really tasty, but also really, really simple. It came from making a few adjustments to a recipe from a flatmate of a good friend of mine in Dunedin (where I studied medicine). We were all students back then, so it uses very basic and inexpensive ingredients, showing that you don't have to get all fancy to make delicious, warming, healthy food. Serves 4

1 onion, finely chopped
½ teaspoon minced red chilli or ¼ teaspoon chilli powder, plus extra to serve (optional)
2 garlic cloves, finely chopped
500 g (1 lb 2 oz) pumpkin, cut into 2 cm (¾ in) dice
1 sweet potato, peeled and cut into 2 cm (¾ in) dice
750 ml (25½ fl oz/3 cups) vegetable stock
125 g (4½ oz/1/2 cup) red lentils
½ bunch fresh coriander (cilantro), roughly chopped, to serve (optional)
freshly ground black pepper, to serve (optional)

Combine the onion, chilli, garlic, pumpkin and sweet potato in a large stockpot set over a medium–low heat. Add a splash of stock and cook for 5 minutes.

Add the vegetable stock and simmer gently for 10 minutes. Add the red lentils and cook for a further 10 minutes.

Transfer to a blender and blitz the soup until smooth.

If you're feeling fancy, garnish with a little coriander and some freshly ground black pepper – perhaps even a few chilli flakes if you like it spicy (I do!).

DR MICHAEL KLAPER

I first met Dr Klaper at a speaking event in Melbourne during his Australian tour. I was a couple of months into my year of eating potatoes and we had a great little chat about that. The following year, I was on stage speaking at Dr McDougall's 'Advanced Study Weekend' (a lifetime highlight, see page 19) and was momentarily star struck when I noticed Dr Klaper in the audience, seemingly enjoying himself. The following day, I had the honour of being invited for a tour of True North Health Center with the great man, which became a very memorable afternoon for me.

The teacher in me is especially appreciative of Dr Klaper's ability to break down the most technical aspects of nutrition and health, making it accessible and easy for the rest of us to understand and put into action. Dr Klaper has appeared in multiple documentaries and speaks regularly all around the world. Albert Einstein said 'If you can't explain it simply, you don't understand it well enough'. Dr Klaper can, and does.

AVO SPUD

My wife Alese has a magical way with potatoes, and she has a real winner with this 'avo-spud'. Serves 1

1 large white potato, baked
½ ripe avocado
1 teaspoon dried parsley
sea salt and freshly ground black pepper

Scoop out the potato flesh into a bowl and mash it with the avocado. Mix in the dried parsley, salt and pepper, then return the mashed filling to the potato skins and serve. Yum!

FOCUS ON FIBRE
by Andrew

There is so much emphasis placed on the quantity of carbohydrates, fat and protein we should eat. Most diet plans tend to focus on one or two of these and exclude the others, and fibre is often the unsung hero. It is well documented that populations with the highest fibre intake also have the lowest rates of heart disease, many cancers and a host of other chronic illnesses. Not only that, but fibre provides bulk to foods and has no digestible calories, meaning you can eat as much high-fibre food as you like and feel full for longer while also losing weight. Oils, processed sugars and flours, along with meat, dairy and eggs contain no fibre at all. Eat more unprocessed beans, whole grains, fruits and veggies to increase your fibre intake.

DR MONICA AGGARWAL

As a very hard-working cardiologist and devoted mother of two, Dr Aggarwal admits that she gave all of her time to these roles while neglecting her own health and wellbeing. She burned the candle at both ends for too long and it finally caught up with her.

Dr Aggarwal's path to lifestyle medicine began with an intense and debilitating struggle against rheumatoid arthritis. She was struck down in her prime and forced to re-evaluate the way she was living. In the process, she discovered the power of plants in reducing the inflammation caused by her rheumatoid arthritis.

These days, she is off all medications and smashes out triathlons for fun. She is dedicated to helping others achieve medication-free health and vitality, and she leads by example.

SWEET POTATO HUMMUS

I think sweet potatoes are some of the most important root vegetables. They are super filling, loaded with potassium, magnesium, a little calcium and B vitamins. I often tell my patients to eat a sweet potato when they feel hungry during the day. It's a filling complex vegetable, and it also satisfies the craving for something sweet. I love hummus as well and eat it literally every day. I have also been feeding hummus to my children since they were nine months old; it is a staple in our house. Naturally, a merger of two of my favourites had to come together in sweet potato hummus. A great snack!

Makes 1.2 kg (2 lb 10 oz)

2 medium sweet potatoes
2 x 400 g (14 oz) tins chickpeas, drained
2 garlic cloves, crushed
¼ teaspoon ground cumin
2 tablespoons tahini (optional)
lemon juice, to taste
sea salt and freshly ground black pepper,
 to taste (optional)

Preheat the oven to 200°C (400°F).

Pierce the sweet potatoes a few times with a fork and place them on a baking tray lined with baking paper. Bake for 45 minutes, or until tender and the flesh is easily pierced with a sharp knife. Set aside to cool, then remove the skin.

Combine the chickpeas, 230 ml (8 fl oz) water and the sweet potato flesh in a blender. Add the crushed garlic, cumin, some salt and pepper and the tahini, if using and lemon juice to taste. (I like black pepper because it gives a nice contrast to the sweetness of the potato.)

Blend to a smooth purée. Adjust the thickness with a little more water if needed. Store in an airtight container in the refrigerator for up to 3 days.

DR RENAE THOMAS

Dr Thomas could sit just as comfortably alongside the athletes in this book. As a former Australian champion in gymnastics, marathon runner and fitness competitor, she's more qualified than most to talk about the intersection between diet and athletic performance, as well as overall health.

Dr Thomas has worked with some of the most influential people and organisations in the world of plant-based nutrition, and is currently doing her four-year residency training, specialising in preventive and family medicine at Loma Linda, California.

Dr Thomas' focus is on helping people to find the sweet spot between modern western medicine, evidence-based nutrition and some good old-fashioned physical exercise.

SWEET POTATO CHOCOLATE CAKE

Serves 8–12

450 g (1 lb/1½ cups) boiled sweet potato chunks
180 g (6½ oz/1 cup) medjool dates, pitted (approximately 20 large)
1 tablespoon reduced balsamic vinegar
1 teaspoon vanilla-bean powder
250 ml (8½ fl oz/1 cup) non-dairy milk of your choice
60–90 g (2–3 oz/½–¾ cup) cacao powder
240 g (8½ oz/1½ cups) sweet potato flour (see Note)
1 teaspoon baking powder
70 g (2½ oz/½ cup) shredded zucchini (courgette)
30 g (1 oz/¼ cup) walnuts (optional; see Note)
fresh berries, to serve (optional)
Icing
165 g (6 oz/¾ cup) peeled, boiled and mashed sweet potato
60 g (2 oz/½ cup) cacao powder
80–180 g (2¾–6½ oz/½–1 cup) medjool dates, pitted (depending on the desired sweetness)
125 g (4½ oz/½ cup) almond, hazelnut or cashew-nut butter (or 1 avocado for a nut-free version)
125 ml (4 fl oz/½ cup) non-dairy milk of your choice

Preheat the oven to 180°C (350°F). Line a 20 cm (8 in) round cake tin with baking paper.

Combine the sweet potato chunks, dates, balsamic, vanilla powder and milk in a high-speed blender and blitz until smooth.

Sift the cacao powder, sweet potato flour and baking powder into a large mixing bowl. Stir in the zucchini and walnuts, if using. Add the sweet potato mixture and stir until just combined.

Pour the mixture into the prepared tin and bake for approximately 40 minutes to 1 hour, or until a skewer inserted in the middle of the cake comes out clean. Transfer to a wire rack to cool completely.

To make the icing, blend all the ingredients together until smooth in a food processor or high-speed blender. Spread over the cake and garnish with fresh berries, if desired.

Note

If you cannot find sweet potato flour, you can substitute it with other grain-free options, such as banana flour or chestnut flour. Alternatively, you can use 185 g (6½ oz/1½ cups) steel-cut oats blitzed into oat flour, though the cake will no longer be grain-free.

Adding walnuts to this cake will increase the fat content.

This cake is particularly good with a scoop of banana 'nicecream'; blended frozen banana and vanilla-bean powder.

LUCY STEGLEY
DOCTORS FOR NUTRITION

The not-for-profit organisation, Doctors For Nutrition, was co-founded in 2018. With medical practitioner ambassadors across Australia, New Zealand and globally, Doctors For Nutrition's mission is to 'bring food back to healthcare' through advocacy, education and research on the benefits of a whole food, plant-based diet.

From hospital menu makeovers, to government health policy overhauls, academic medical curriculum updates and much more, Doctors For Nutrition has ambitious plans. Its annual 'Nutrition in Healthcare Conference' will be the main event for qualified experts to share the science and practical implementation of a plant-based diet with their peers and the general public.

One of the DFN co-founders, Lucy Stegley, has created this recipe. Lucy has been a powerhouse of the plant-based movement in Australia over the last decade. She ran the world's first vegan university cafeteria at the Royal Melbourne Institute of Technology, and has organised many public events and lecture series with internationally renowned speakers to promote the message of good health to the masses.

CAULI–POTATO MASH w MUSHROOM MACADAMIA GRAVY

Gravy need not clog your arteries with damaging, animal-derived cholesterol. Herbs and miso paste impart an earthy, rich flavour to this plant-based gravy, while blended macadamia nuts add healthy, whole fats. Adding parboiled cauliflower florets to the mash makes the texture lighter and helps you tick another vegetable off your daily 'doctor's orders' prescription. Try to reduce your exposure to agricultural chemicals by choosing organic ingredients wherever possible. **Serves 4**

Mash
500 g (1 lb 2 oz/4 cups) peeled and cubed
  potatoes (such as King Edwards or Colibans)
250 g (9 oz/2 cups) cauliflower florets
1 garlic clove, minced
1 tablespoon plant-based milk of your choice
pinch of sea salt
Gravy
205 g (7 oz/1½ cups) roughly chopped leek
(white part only)
1 shallot, chopped
2 heaped teaspoons dark miso paste (such
as Genmai Aka, which is made from a
combination of soy beans and brown rice)
2 garlic cloves, minced
1 teaspoon roughly chopped sage
1 teaspoon roughly chopped thyme, plus extra
sprigs to garnish
½ teaspoon finely chopped rosemary, plus
extra sprigs to garnish
180 g (6½ oz/2 cups) button mushrooms,
roughly chopped
3 tablespoons plant-based milk of your choice
80 g (2¾ oz/½ cup) macadamias or cashew
nuts (see Note)
1–2 teaspoons tamari (optional)

Put the potato in a saucepan and cover with cold water. Bring to the boil over a high heat and simmer until tender and the flesh is easily pierced with a fork.

While the potatoes are boiling, make the gravy. Heat a frying pan over a low heat and sauté the chopped leek and shallot in a little water for approximately 5 minutes, stirring and adding additional water as needed to prevent sticking. Add the miso paste, garlic and herbs and simmer for another few minutes. Add the mushrooms and cook until tender.

When the potatoes are starting to soften, add the cauliflower florets to the water and boil until tender (2–3 minutes).

Drain the potatoes and cauliflower, then place them back in the pot with the minced garlic, milk and salt. Mash until well combined and quite smooth. Set aside with the lid on to keep the mash warm.

Combine the sautéed vegetables with the milk and macadamias in a high-speed blender and blend until smooth. Add a splash or two of tamari if you like your gravy a little saltier and darker in colour. Blend in some more milk or water to thin the gravy if necessary.

Place the mashed potatoes in a big bowl, pour the gravy on top and garnish with sprigs of herbs. The gravy works well as a sauce for other vegetables too, and it can also be used as a dip!

Note

If you like, pre-soak the macadamias in water for a few hours before using, then drain and rinse.

DR MICHAEL GREGER

Dr Michael Greger is an unstoppable force in nutrition science and education. His reach and his dedication to sharing important, life-saving information is unparalleled. His website, 'NutritionFacts.org', has been endlessly helpful to me and countless others, and I have no idea how many times I've visited it to have my questions answered by his myriad science-based videos on a huge number of health topics.

A founding member and Fellow of the American College of Lifestyle Medicine (ACLM), he is a physician and internationally-recognised speaker on nutrition, food safety and public health issues. He has lectured at the Conference on World Affairs, testified before Congress and was an expert witness in the defence of Oprah Winfrey in the infamous 'meat defamation' trial.

In 2017, Dr Greger was honoured with the ACLM Lifestyle Medicine Trailblazer Award. His latest book, 'How Not to Die', became an instant New York Times Best Seller. With so many people being led astray by questionable information on the internet, it's reassuring to know that Dr Greger is out there doing his best to make 'Dr Google' obsolete.

STUFFED SWEET POTATOES BALSAMIC DATE GLAZE

I love sweet potatoes, they're one of the healthiest foods on the planet. The purple ones are the best due to their anti-inflammatory and antioxidant properties, and you can usually find them at Asian supermarkets and health-food stores. They're so good that I send them out in the mail as Christmas gifts! Here's a recipe for a stocking stuffer you can actually stuff. **Serves 4**

4 medium sweet potatoes
35 g (1¼ oz/½ cup) fresh or frozen peas, steamed
2 tablespoons finely chopped chives or spring onions (scallions)
30 g (1 oz/¼ cup) raw slivered almonds
freshly ground black pepper
Balsamic date glaze (see Note)
80 g (2¾ oz/½ cup) pitted dates
185 ml (6 fl oz/¾ cup) warm water
125 ml (4 fl oz/½ cup) balsamic vinegar

Preheat the oven to 200°C (400°F).

Place the sweet potatoes on a baking tray and prick them a few times with a fork. Bake for about 1 hour, or until tender and easily pierced with a sharp knife. Transfer the potatoes to a chopping board and leave to cool slightly. Keep the oven on.

To make the glaze, combine the dates and warm water in a small bowl and set aside for about 10 minutes to soften. Transfer the dates and their soaking water to a blender, add the balsamic and blitz until smooth. Pour into a small saucepan and bring to the boil over a medium–high heat, then reduce the heat to low and simmer, stirring frequently, until the glaze has thickened and reduced.

Cut each sweet potato in half lengthways and scoop out the flesh, leaving about ½ cm (¼ in) of flesh attached to the skin.

Combine the flesh, peas and chives in a bowl and mix well. Spoon the mixture back into the potato halves and return the stuffed potatoes to the oven. Bake for another 15 minutes, or until heated through.

To serve, sprinkle the potatoes with the almonds, drizzle over some balsamic date glaze and finish with a few grinds of black pepper.

Note

This glaze is delicious drizzled over your favourite roasted vegetables or grain dishes, as well as fruits, such as watermelon or strawberries.

DR MALCOLM MACKAY

I didn't want to approach just any doctor with my idea to eat only potatoes for a year. I tracked Dr Mackay down, as I knew he was an advocate of the whole food, plant-based diet and would know more about plant-based nutrition and its impact on health than most doctors. I had a feeling he would be a potato fan, too.

Malcolm turned out to be the perfect choice. Initially, I think he thought my idea was a bit weird (who wouldn't?!), but he didn't baulk at it and was happy to support me through the year. It was great to have him in my corner, keeping on top of all my testing and medical check-ups, and providing peace of mind for my worrying wife at various stages. I might have even helped him confront his own fears when he appeared on prime time TV with me!

Malcolm's wife Jenny Cameron was there every step of the way too. She's a nutritionist and research librarian with a seemingly insatiable thirst for knowledge of human nutrition. She helped Malcolm to understand the completeness of the nutrition available in potatoes, and I've had many great discussions with her about human health since. We even went halfway around the world to attend Dr McDougall's 'Advanced Study Weekend' together (see page 19).

SIMPLE SPUDS ON THE GO

by Jenny Cameron

Andrew's year of potatoes has influenced our own eating habits, and these days we often find ourselves using potatoes as our go-to snack food when travelling, eating out, or even just to have on hand when the 'hungries' hit late in the afternoon.

Every other day, we bake a tray of them – sometimes whole, sometimes as wedges – and whereas once upon a time we may have wanted our potatoes warm and covered in sauce or other condiments, now we find that if we are hungry, they taste great cold and plain!

Malcolm always carries a zip-lock bag of spuds out skiing and has been known to eat them on a chairlift or just standing out on the ski slope. Whenever we travel on a long-haul flight, we bring a bag of cooked potatoes, and have even been known to go to restaurants with potatoes hidden in my handbag and, when the typical very-low-calorie 'special meal' is served (usually a salad with little or no starches), we sneak them out and place them under the salad.

HOW POTATOES AFFECTED ANDREW'S HEALTH

BY DR MALCOLM MACKAY, GENERAL PRACTITIONER

Andrew consulted me during the first week of his all-potato diet and I agreed to provide medical support for his project/adventure. I guess he chose me as his doctor because of my advocacy for the health benefits of a whole food, plant-based diet, and my familiarity with the 'starch-based diet' of Dr John McDougall (see page 19). However, I did not understand the idea of a mono-diet for food addiction, and I suggested adding greens and berries to his potato diet – potentially introducing some unwanted moderation to the mission.

I went home and found that my partner in life and plant-based nutritionist, Jenny, had previously prepared several spreadsheets of the nutrient profiles one would get from eating a full day's calories of a single type of food, and one of these was potatoes. It looked almost complete. Vitamin A (carotenoids) appeared lacking, and so, at the next visit, I suggested that Andrew include sweet potato as a de facto potato variety and he was agreeable to this.

At no stage did I consider an all-potato diet to be 'dangerous', as one health expert suggested. Potatoes are rich in carbohydrates – the preferred fuel for the human body – and the protein content is moderate and close to the recommended intake. They contain dietary fibre and a wide range of nutrients, but nothing in excess. I would have been more concerned if Andrew were using high-protein, meal-replacement shakes to lose weight – this, I would consider 'dangerous'. The main hazards of eating only potatoes are unwanted weight loss – potatoes are bulky and low in calories – and getting healthier quicker than your doctor can reduce your blood pressure and diabetes medications, leading to excessive medication effects.

I had lingering concerns that Andrew might develop some rare micronutrient deficiency after many months of eating only potatoes. From time to time, I reviewed the food composition data for potatoes and we would test nutrients that appeared to be lacking from potatoes – vitamin B6 and essential fatty acids, for example, and the results would be normal (Andrew took a vitamin B12 supplement in preference to leaving some soil on his potatoes). Nutrient analysis tables and software are only as good as the database they are built on, and my experience with the potato analysis illustrates that sometimes the potential nutrient deficiency is in the data rather than the food, particularly for trace elements such as iodine and selenium. Nutrient analysis and blood tests are only part of the assessment. Clinical signs – general health, changes to skin, mucous membranes of the mouth, etc. – are an essential part of assessment of nutrient adequacy, and these remained normal for Andrew throughout the year.

Jenny and I were on a Dr McDougall Adventure Holiday when Andrew's potato-only diet hit the national and US media. We tipped off Dr McDougall and, before long, he was on US national television speaking in support of Andrew's year of potatoes.

The health improvements I observed were spectacular. LDL 'bad' cholesterol fell by 50 per cent to 1.3 mmol/l (50 mg/dl) and stayed there – that's better than my patients on statins, who often don't reach their target value of less than 1.8. Triglycerides and HDL remained at healthy levels. Andrew's glucose and HbA1c (measure of blood-sugar control over time) defied the 'low-carb diet' rhetoric, indicating excellent blood-sugar control for the entire year that he followed the very high carbohydrate, low-fat diet of potatoes. This case study also downgrades the relevance of the glycaemic index (GI) to starch-based diets, as high-GI foods like potatoes are considered to adversely affect blood-sugar control.

When you stick to a diet based on low-calorie-density foods, like potatoes, excess body fat gradually melts away without the need for portion control or mindful eating. When you feel hungry, you just eat more potatoes. Potatoes lack the sugar, fat, salt and high calorie content that characterise addictive foods. The average person would need to eat 3–4 kg (6 lg 10 oz–8 lb 13 oz) of potatoes per day just to maintain their weight. Andrew's large frame shed 53 kg (116 lb) in one year; more than a third of his body weight

– far better than the current medical target of 5–10 per cent achieved with weight-loss drugs and smaller portions of the same calorie-rich food that led to the excess weight. Andrew's weight loss was on a par with bariatric surgery but without the complications that accompany surgical procedures that cause permanent damage to a perfectly normal gut. The problem with most weight-loss programs, even bariatric surgery, is that people regain the weight they lost when they return to their old eating habits. Andrew was not going to do this – taking a quote from 'The Matrix', 'You've been down that road before, you know where it leads, and I know it's not where you want to be'. The all-potato diet had reset his taste for food and he was able to enjoy a whole food, plant-based diet built on whole grains, legumes, vegetables (including potatoes, of course), fruit and small quantities of the more calorie-dense nuts and seeds. When people eat this type of food, they become lean and healthy – it's simple and predictable.

I did not foresee some of the other qualitative improvements in Andrew's life. His depression and hopelessness lifted, and he was able fully engage with his family and friends and take an active role in coaching others to transform their health. As often happens, the change to a whole food, plant-based diet led to an increase in energy and a spontaneous desire to exercise – I call it 'the half-marathon effect'. Sure enough, Andrew ran a marathon during the following year.

I have learnt a lot from Andrew about behavioural change and food. I often use that Matrix quote when counselling patients on maintaining alcohol and substance abstinence. The 'moderation' concept that had failed Andrew in the past is a terrible strategy for diet and health behaviours, as most of us are not good at moderation. Eating potatoes (or other low-calorie whole foods such as fruit) before the calorie-rich indulgence was another great strategy that Jenny and I teach at our seminars. Andrew also identified a flaw in human behaviour – discounting the future cost in favour of the short-term gains – and applied an upgrade by becoming mindful that the enjoyment of the next 10 minutes may not outweigh the remorse that follows or the long-term poor health of repeating the poor food choice.

I advocate a whole food, plant-based diet as a science-based strategy for a longer, healthier life. The transition to whole-plant foods is full of pitfalls of moderation and our natural tendency to seek the richest foods that almost fit our eating plan. The all-potato diet is an excellent transition strategy as it is safe, the rules are black and white, and the ease of high adherence leads to an earlier experience of wellbeing, and nothing tastes better than good health.

HEALTH PROFESSIONALS

Dietitians and nutritionists play a hugely valuable role in society as the conduits between the scientific community and the rest of us. They take the valuable information gained through key studies and apply it in the real world in a form that we can understand and put into action. The people in this chapter understand how our choices affect our health, and they know the importance of having a solid and simple plan that can provide the body with all the essential nutrients it needs to thrive.

As advocates of a whole food, plant-based diet, it's no surprise that these health professionals are all major fans of potatoes and include them as a key pillar of a healthy diet. You'll notice that in contrast to the doctors, these recipes are more attention-grabbing to get people excited and enthusiastic about diet change.

HOWARD JACOBSON

Howard Jacobson has co-authored some of my absolute favourite books, including 'Proteinaholic' by Garth Davis and 'Whole' by T. Colin Campbell.

I was already feeling pretty star-struck when Chef AJ (see page 117) invited me to her place for dinner one night when I was visiting LA. At dinner, I mentioned that I wanted to write a book. She said, 'oh, Howie could help you with that!' Before I knew it, I was on the phone with the man himself! I was amazed that he was so willing to take time out of his day to give some help and advice to little ol' me.

I know that I'm very far from the only person he has helped. Howard is so passionate in giving his time and expertise to help those who need it most. Through his writing, his amazing interviews on the 'Plant Yourself' podcast, and now through 'WellStart Health', he's helped countless people take control of their own destiny.

Howard's goals include shaking up healthcare, sharing how delicious and joyful a healthy life can be, saving the planet and reintroducing people to their most authentic, bipedal, plant-eating, anti-fragile selves. And, one day, making the perfect potato wedge.

RECIPE FOR APPRECIATING THE HUMBLE POTATO

HOWARD JACOBSON, PHD, CHIEF OF BEHAVIORAL SCIENCE, WELLSTARHEALTH.COM

I'm no chef, and pretty much everything I eat is so simple that it's not worth turning it into recipes (e.g. boil potato, put it on a plate, add some salsa and eat).

So, when Andrew asked me to contribute a recipe to this book, I offered a recipe for making the transition to a Spud Fit diet as elegant and sustainable as possible. Here are the ingredients...

1. Understand the science

2. Find a community

3. Rely on current favourites

4. Eat more

5. Give yourself time

6. Embrace simplicity

7. Have fun

Now, let's look at each of these in turn.

1. UNDERSTAND THE SCIENCE

Once you embark on a Spud Fit kind of life, you are going to freak people the fuck out. I know otherwise rational people who recoil from potatoes like they were Satan's boogers. They will quote you from ketogenic and paleo websites and authors to show you why you can't possibly be experiencing what you are, in fact, experiencing.

Until you experience the wonders of a starch-based diet for yourself, you'll be vulnerable to these opinions. At this stage, the best defence is having faith; not necessarily in yourself, but in the underlying science supporting the Spud Fit diet.

So, don't just take Andrew's word for the benefits of a high-starch diet on cardiovascular health, blood glucose stabilisation and weight. Check out the diets of the leanest, healthiest, longest-lived populations on earth. Are they keto warriors, or rice-potato-pasta-yam freaks? What is the human body designed to consume? What do we

prefer – fruit or raw meat? What do our bodies use as primary fuel – carbohydrates or protein? What stops insulin from shuttling sugar from our bloodstream into our muscle cells – baked potatoes or French fries?

2. FIND A COMMUNITY

OK, so you've got science on your side. That's a great first step, but it's usually not enough to withstand the onslaught of the spud-phobic masses who didn't have a negative word to say about your shitty McDonald's diet, but got apoplexy when you announced that you were going to cut back or eliminate meat and processed food.

A patently false opinion, echoed by everyone around us, affects us way more than we might think.

Some interested mid-twentieth centuries studies by psychologist Solomon Asch highlighted how susceptible we are to this kind of relentless peer pressure, even when we absolutely 100 per cent know that we're right.

In a version of Asch's study, participants were asked which of three lines was the same length as a reference line. One line was and obvious match – there was no ambiguity about the question.

The twist was that the participant was put in a group of six people where the other five were all confederates of the researcher. And all of them, one after the other, said that the shorter line was actually longer. The real participant always went sixth, so they were exposed to a unanimous wrong answer. Over the entire experiment, 75 per cent of the participants were swayed to choose the incorrect answer at least once.

So, even when we're sure about the facts, we will cave to peer pressure like a politician to a lobbyist if we don't surround ourselves with people who speak truth.

Find a community that supports a whole food, plant-based diet. Join that community and stay engaged. Attend meetups and potlucks and lectures. If online, visit and post frequently. In an insane world, find a sane bubble and relax there from time to time.

3. RELY ON CURRENT FAVOURITES

When I spent time in South Africa, I tried to learn how to drive over there. I was a fine driver in the US (above average, I'll have you know), but the first twist in South Africa was driving on the left-hand side of the road. It took a while to get used to that.

The second twist was that the vehicle my family had rented had, like almost every vehicle in Africa, a manual transmission. As someone who had never driven a stick before, that was an ordeal on its own. 'Shift!' my wife would scream as I slammed down the accelerator and revved into the red zone.

The third twist was the fact that the only rental vehicle we could find in Johannesburg was a 16-seater combi, which was about twice the length of anything I'd driven up to that point. Attempting to parallel park that thing was a show that sadists the world over would pay good money to watch.

Any one of those twists was manageable. But, when all three were combined, my brain couldn't handle the new variables. And so, I gave up, much to the relief of my children, who will surely need years of therapy in the future to overcome that experience.

As you transition to a new way of eating, you can easily get overwhelmed by all the unfamiliar elements. New ingredients, new ways of thinking about your plate, new styles of cooking (oil-free, for example). So, it's crucial to keep as many constants as possible.

Love pizza? Mash a potato into a pizza shape and bake it, then cover it with veggies and tomato sauce.

Enjoy Mexican dishes? Go for those. Italian? Thai? Stick to the flavour profiles you know and love, and swap out the meat, dairy and processed junk for the good stuff. Once you've mastered a twist, add another.

4. EAT MORE

It's simple maths: when you shift from a calorically dense diet of animal products and processed foods to a whole, plant-based diet, it's easy to under consume. Think of it this way: if all you ate was broccoli and your basal metabolic rate (the energy you expend just resting and being a human body) is 2000 calories per day, then you'd need to eat about 8 kg (19 lb) broccoli to balance the ledger. Basically, eating broccoli would become your full-time job.

That's an extreme case, of course, but even if you go mega-Spud Fit and eat nothing but potatoes, that's still almost 3 kg (6 lb) potatoes per day.

Here's the point: to get enough calories to power you and keep you alert and energised, you will have to up your quantities. If you're going Spud Fit to lose weight, that may seem like the exact wrong strategy. After all, the mantra of weight loss in our crazy culture is 'eat less'. But, as you know, deprivation doesn't work because it can't last. You're fighting against your own biology, just as surely as if you tried to go on a 'stop urinating' protocol. Knock yourself out with willpower and discipline – I guarantee you'll be pissing like a racehorse within a few hours.

When you eat a natural human diet, you don't need to restrict yourself or engage in portion control or timed feeding to get to your ideal weight. No other animal struggles to inhibit their food intake. Eat your natural diet, and you won't either.

5. GIVE YOURSELF TIME

Here's a dirty little secret of healthy eating: potatoes don't taste as good as bacon. At least, not at first.

While those of us who have adopted a whole food, plant-based diet love what we're eating, and can approach orgasm through a Honeycrisp apple, we didn't start that way. We had to accept that our new diet was going to be bland compared to the shits and giggles we were used to.

Essentially, when we eat for pleasure rather than health, we're getting high on shots of dopamine that our brain squirts out when we 'hit the jackpot' and find a rare cache of calories. Like all addictions, we neuro-adapt and end up needing more and more sugar, salt and fat to give us the same high.

When we come down from that high and choose healthy foods, our tastebuds go around in mourning for a while. Give them between three weeks and three months to return to normal. When you bite into a Honeycrisp apple and have the urge to get a room, you'll know you're there.

6. EMBRACE SIMPLICITY

I know this is a book of recipes, but you don't need to rely on recipes to eat well. The simpler you make your meals, the more likely you are to make positive, health-promoting choices.

Bake a potato. Throw some steamed greens on that sucker and add a sauce.

Roast or air-fry some potato wedges with herbs and garlic powder. Steam some broccoli.

Develop a repertoire of meals so simple that you'd be embarrassed to call them 'recipes'. Keep those staples on hand. Practice making them often.

7. HAVE FUN

Joy is a necessary nutrient, just as much as Vitamin C or beta-carotene. Keep this journey light and happy. Don't get dour or serious. When you slip up, become a curious scientist rather than your own personal prosecutor.

And share the fun. As you get better at preparing and eating the Spud Fit way, invite others to sample your creations. Use your increased energy and better mood to do fun and exciting things, to spend time with people you love and to find and fulfill your purpose on this planet.

Enjoy, and good luck!

TIM STEELE

A few weeks into my year-long Spud Fit challenge, I received a very cool email from Tim Steele who wanted to assure me that I was on the right track with potatoes and that he had done a lot of research to back it up. He was just disappointed that I hadn't done my challenge earlier so that I could be featured in the 'Icons' chapter of his new book 'The Potato Hack', which was due to be released in a few weeks.

Of course, we became email friends and have kept in regular contact ever since. It's been really great to have Tim in my corner always ready and willing to offer helpful advice. His major focus is on how potatoes help to create the ideal conditions in the gut for our good bacteria to thrive. Good health starts with our gut bacteria and intestinal health, and Tim believes (and I agree) that potatoes are the perfect food for happy guts. Tim coined a phrase in his book that I've used many times since reading it: 'If you're not hungry enough to eat a plain, cold, boiled potato, then you're not hungry!"

POTATO: SOUP—ER FOOD

♟♟♟♟♟♟

This recipe lends itself to unlimited variations. The most important step is the puréeing, as this makes a thick, velvety broth. **Serves 4**

2–3 large potatoes
350 ml (12 fl oz) vegetable stock
sea salt, freshly ground black pepper and spices of your choice, to taste
45 g (1½ oz/½ cup) chopped mushrooms (optional)
40 g (1½ oz/¼ cup) chopped onions (optional)
2 tablespoons chopped flat-leaf (Italian) parsley

Cut the potatoes into 2.5 cm (1 in) cubes and boil in the vegetable stock until tender. Add seasoning and spices to taste.

Remove 250 ml (8½ fl oz/1 cup) of the soup and place in a blender. Blitz to a purée, then return to the pot and bring the soup to the boil.

Add the mushrooms and onion, and continue boiling for another 2–3 minutes. Remove from the heat and serve garnished with chopped parsley.

ANTHONY DISSEN

Anthony's message resonated deeply with me from the moment I first came across his work a couple of years ago. Highly educated in both eastern and western theories and philosophies of healthy lifestyles, he combines them all seamlessly in a way that's easy for the layman to connect with. He understands the importance of plant-based nutrition, but also knows that knowledge is wasted without individual empowerment; there is so much information and advice out there that it often leaves us more confused and, as a result, we remain stagnant.

Anthony inspires action through his holistic approach and his belief that the true power to heal, grow and expand as human beings is an innate quality we all share and contain without ourselves.

PORTUGUESE CALDO VERDE

Heat a large stockpot over a medium heat and add the onion, garlic, salt and pepper, with 60 ml (2 fl oz/¼ cup water). Cook, stirring regularly, for 5–7 minutes, or until the onions are translucent. If the onions are beginning to stick, add more water as necessary.

Next, add the potato and about half of the collard greens. Add 1.5 litres (51 fl oz/6 cups) water and stir to combine. Bring to the boil, cover, and simmer for about 30 minutes, or until the potatoes are soft and the greens are very tender.

Working in batches, transfer the soup to a blender and blitz until smooth. Alternatively, use a hand-held blender.

Pour the soup into a clean stockpot and add the remaining collard greens. Place over a medium heat and simmer for another 5–10 minutes, or until the greens are bright green and tender. Adjust the seasoning if necessary, then ladle into bowls and enjoy!

This is one of my absolute favourite soups. To me, this soup personifies what a healthy, nutrient-dense diet should look like: dishes full of complex carbohydrates, filling starches, dark, leafy greens and lots of onion and garlic. While the classic caldo verde (meaning 'green broth' in Portuguese) contains oil and cooked pork, this version celebrates the healthiest components of the dish while removing the processed and animal-based ingredients. This soup is also amazingly simple to prepare, which is helpful for incorporating whole food, plant-based dishes into your diet. I was first introduced to it by my partner's family, who were all born and raised in Portugal, and it has been a lot of fun to take a classic Portuguese dish and show them a healthier version to make at home. Warm and comforting and full of flavour, this is a great way to showcase the power of the potato! Aproveite esta sopa! Serves 6–8

1 onion, roughly chopped
6 garlic cloves, minced
½ teaspoon sea salt
¼ teaspoon freshly ground black pepper
5–6 white potatoes, chopped
450 g (1 lb) Tuscan kale (cavolo nero) or collard greens, de-stemmed and sliced into thin strips
1.5 litres (51 fl oz/6 cups) water

DEREK SIMNETT

Derek is another person who would be equally at home in the Athletes section of this book. He's a nutritionist who also places a huge emphasis on physical exercise and fitness, and he certainly walks the walk. His fuel is simple and delicious, and his 'muscle meals' are always crowd-pleasing while providing the perfect fuel for athletic performance and vitality. I really appreciate Derek's approach to food as a tool to help us get the best out of life. He's often quoted, saying 'food is fuel, where will it take you?'

MISO BAKED POTATOES w PEAS

🍴🍴🍴🍴🍴🍴

I love this recipe because it is simple and absolutely delicious. Miso is so versatile, has great health benefits and pairs really well with potatoes! These baked potatoes are amazing as a side dish or used as a main.
Serves 2

8–10 medium yellow or red potatoes, cubed
235 g (8½ oz/1½ cups) frozen peas
Miso sauce
¼ red onion
2 tablespoons miso paste
2 tablespoons whole linseeds (flaxseeds)
1 tablespoon stone-ground mustard
1 tablespoon apple-cider vinegar
1–2 garlic cloves

Preheat the oven to 190°C (375°F).

Combine the miso sauce ingredients in a high-speed blender with 125 ml (4 fl oz/½ cup) water and blitz until smooth.

Put the cubed potatoes in a mixing bowl, pour in the sauce and mix until evenly coated.

Transfer the potatoes to a large, glass baking dish and bake for 30 minutes. Give the potatoes a stir, then bake for another 20 minutes.

Add the frozen peas, mix well, then bake for a final 10 minutes, or until the peas are soft and cooked through. Serve immediately.

SOCIAL SITUATIONS
by Andrew

We want change to be easy and comfortable. We want change to be smooth and seamless. We don't want it to upset the apple cart in any way, and we sure as hell don't want anyone to think we are strange or question what we are doing. 'But what about going to restaurants and other social situations?' is one of the most common questions I get. Many people are worried about causing trouble or being the odd one out. We trick ourselves into thinking it's all harder than it needs to be, mostly because we are afraid. Don't be afraid, be assertive! Nobody ever got ahead in life by going along with the crowd. Ask for what you want and, if you can't get it, then make it happen for yourself. You'll feel great in the knowledge that you've made a decision based on what's right for you rather than opting for what's easy and 'safe'.

 Some tips for dining out:

 Check the menu online before you go and decide what you'll have when there's no pressure. Putting together some different sides is usually a safe bet, however being a chef is a creative job, and in my experience they welcome the chance to do something outside their usual menu, as it's an opportunity to flex their creative muscle. Call ahead - give them a chance to prepare and, more often than not, you'll be pleasantly surprised.

 If you're nervous, tell them that you have an allergy or that you're on doctor's orders. Plant foods are cheap - especially rice and potatoes, so if you tell them you'll pay for a full main course they'll be happy to take your money!

 Fill up before you go! I aways eat a couple of potatoes before I go out for a meal so that I'm not super hungry and will be easily fed.

 If you're going to someone's house, then help them out with a few ideas for what they could make that everyone can enjoy. Offer to bring a dish or two with you – maybe a side dish or a salad. Look at this as a chance to show your friends how great plant-based eating can be!

 Bring some baked potatoes in foil with you as a back-up plan, so that if all else fails you can still eat something healthy and not go hungry.

KATHY ASHTON
FLOURISH LIVE NATURALLY

Kathy Ashton was the first person to make the suggestion that changing my diet could have been responsible for the dramatic improvement in my mental health. She told me all about how healthy intestinal flora contributes to significant improvements in serotonin production in the gut. Medication tends to focus specifically on hormones produced in the brain, but unbeknownst to me until I met Kathy, my potato-only diet was creating an excellent environment for the feel-good hormones in my gut.

Kathy uses nutritional medicine to help people transform their lives by improving sleep and energy, managing sustainable weight loss and reducing the symptoms of chronic diseases. Kathy believes that good health is only one decision away and starts with the very food you consume. She's an amazing cook too; dinner at the Ashtons' is always an event to remember!

CRUNCHY POTATO BALLS

††††††

This is one of my family's favourite recipes. Super quick and easy to make, you can jazz these up with more herbs and spices, or make them plain and simple. They take the humble mashed spud and turn it into a delicious, hearty, healthy meal. Accompanied by your favourite salad in summer or a vegetable ratatouille in winter, these crunchy potato balls will soon become a staple. They're great to make ahead of time: freeze, take out before work in the morning, and voilà! An easy, yummy dinner when you get home. You can even use a few of them as a burger. Delicious!
Makes 20-25 balls

5 large white unpeeled potatoes, chopped (see note)
1 red onion, centre removed and finely chopped
1 clove garlic, centre removed and finely chopped
1 x 450 g (16 oz) tin white cannellini beans (or other bean of your choosing), rinsed and drained
1 bunch fresh coriander, chopped
1 bunch fresh basil, chopped
1 cup frozen corn kernels, thawed
30g (½ cup/1 oz) nutritional yeast
To serve
salt and pepper
chilli flakes (optional)
fresh tomato salsa, organic tomato sauce, or relish

Place the chopped potatoes into a large pot of cold water. Boil until tender, drain and then mash.

Pre-heat the oven to 180°C (350°F).

When the mash is cool enough to handle, add all the other ingredients and mix thoroughly.

Form the mixture into balls and place onto an oven tray lined with baking paper. Bake until golden brown (20-25 minutes)

Season and topped with fresh tomato salsa, organic tomato sauce or relish and chilli flakes if desired.

Note

You can substitute sweet potatoes if you prefer, or you can do a mixture of both.

MICHELE MARTINEZ

Otherwise known as 'The Fruit Doctor', Michele Martinez lives and breathes the old adage that 'an apple a day keeps the doctor away'. She specialises in helping her clients to reduce or eliminate medications for diabetes, high blood pressure, high cholesterol, feminine problems and more, using a plant-based diet with an emphasis on consuming whole, unprocessed fruit... and potatoes! She's an accomplished chef too, and uses her experience and skill to show people how plants can be exciting and delicious at the same time.

Michele pays attention to how we use food to regulate our emotional state, and how taking control of our lives and developing emotional maturity in a variety of ways can change the way we see and use food.

SCALLOPED POTATOES

This is a great comfort food recipe, a healthy version of an old favourite. Clients of mine rave about this dish and say it helps them to stay plant-based, low-fat and dairy-free. A perfect side dish to a meat-free meatloaf, soup or marinated barbecue 'ribs' recipe made from portobello mushrooms. Serves 4

6 small red potatoes, sliced into discs
30 g (1 oz/½ cup) nutritional yeast
½ tablespoon onion powder
½ tablespoon garlic powder
6 spring onions (scallions), diced
Sauces (choose one)
300 g (10½ oz) silken tofu (1 packet)
or
1 x 400 g (14 oz) tin salt-free white beans, drained
½ cauliflower, steamed
or
60 g (2 oz/½ cup) walnuts
1 potato, peeled and steamed

Steam the potatoes in a steamer basket over a saucepan of simmering water until soft, about 15–20 minutes. Set aside. If you're making the cauliflower sauce, steam the cauliflower the same way, then set aside.

Choose what sauce you would like to make. If you're using the bean or walnut sauces, combine the ingredients with 125 ml (4 fl oz/½ cup) water. For all sauces, add the nutritional yeast, onion and garlic powder, then blitz in a high-speed blender until smooth. Transfer to a small saucepan set over a medium heat and stir until hot.

Place the steamed potatoes in a baking dish and pour your chosen sauce on top. Scatter over the spring onions and serve hot.

NICOLETTE RICHER

Knowledge is power, and Nicolette focuses her efforts on helping people understand just how much power they hold over their own health. Knowledge without action is pointless, and Nicolette has made it her mission to help the world make powerful decisions with every mouthful. She helps transform people with chronic illness into conquerors of their condition through nutrition, detoxification and positive, stress-shifting tools. She wants everyone to know how human health and environmental health are inextricably linked.

Nicolette is so full of energy and enthusiasm that it's hard not to get excited about whole foods when in her presence.

BAKED POTATO w THREE SAUCES

¥¥¥¥¥¥¥

Serves 1

1 medium potato

Preheat the oven to 180°C (350°F).
Gently wash the potato in cold, running water, being careful not to damage the skin as so many good nutrients live directly underneath. Make sure to remove any sprouts or dark spots.
Pierce the potato a few times with a fork and bake directly on the oven rack for 1–1½ hours, or until soft.
Remove from the oven, slice the potato in half and top with one of the following sauces.

Accidental favourite

This dressing can be cooked or served raw, blended or left chunky – whatever you please; it's very versatile! With warm, tropical flavours, it can be used in so many ways: spooned over a bowl of steamed rice, tossed with roasted veggies or blended with roasted potatoes to create a thick soup, sauce or a puréed veggie side dish.

Ginger is excellent for relieving nausea and improving digestion. If you've been having stomach troubles lately, enjoy this dressing with some simple steamed veggies, along with a cup of ginger tea with a little maple syrup.

Makes 500 ml (17 fl oz/2 cups)

1 garlic head

3 tomatoes

1 apple, cored

½ medium onion

2.5 cm (1 in) piece fresh ginger, peeled and finely diced

80 ml (2½ fl oz/⅓ cup) apple-cider vinegar

zest and juice of 1 orange

¼ avocado, roughly chopped (optional)

1 tablespoon maple syrup (optional)

1 bunch coriander (cilantro), roughly chopped

Preheat the oven to 180°C (350°F).

Snip the top off the garlic head to expose the cloves, then rinse well.

Dice the tomatoes, apple and onion.

Combine the ginger, head of garlic, apple, tomato and onion in a casserole dish with a splash of water. Bake for about 25 minutes, or until tender. Remove from the oven and leave to cool a little.

Transfer to a blender, add the apple-cider vinegar, orange zest and juice and avocado and maple syrup (if using). Blend to a smooth purée.

Add the coriander, if using, then pulse a couple of times until just incorporated, or blitz if you want a salsa verde-like dressing.

Notes

If you're short on time, skip cooking the vegetables and create a raw dressing instead. Just finely dice all of your ingredients and combine in a blender, or just add to a jar and shake well.

Serve this dressing over roasted sweet potatoes, parsnips or yams, or use it as a garnish for puréed pumpkin (squash).

Tango salsa

This chunky dressing will get you dancing across the kitchen floor; the flavours sing!

Pair this salsa with linseed (flaxseed) crackers or kale chips, eat it straight from the bowl like a chopped salad, or try it as a topping for baked potatoes.

Tomatoes are a great source of biotin for healthy nails and shiny hair, and Vitamin K, which regulates blood clotting, assists with injury and wound healing, and helps to transport calcium around your body. Seriously, what would we do without tomatoes?

Makes 500 ml (17 fl oz/2 cups)

4 tomatoes, diced (yellow and red heirloom varieties, if available)

½ bunch coriander (cilantro), roughly chopped

2 garlic cloves, finely chopped

80 ml (2½ fl oz/⅓ cup) freshly squeezed lime juice (approx. 4 limes)

60 ml (2 fl oz/¼ cup) apple-cider vinegar

1 tablespoon maple syrup (optional)

¼ avocado, roughly chopped (optional)

Combine the tomato, coriander, garlic and lime juice in a large jar. Add the apple-cider vinegar and maple syrup and avocado, if using

Screw the lid on tight and shake vigorously until nicely blended. If you want a smoother dressing, combine all the ingredients in a blender and blitz until smooth.

Notes

If you like tropical flavours, add some chopped mango or pineapple. For an Italian-inspired dressing, replace the coriander with basil, similar to a Caprese salad. Or, alternatively, add some diced capsicums (bell peppers) and red onion for extra crunch.

Shaken, not stirred

A simple shaken dressing, delicious drizzled on a baked, mashed or steamed potato, or any type of hot or cold vegetable dish. Blast the song Skyfall by Adele while you're making it, and do your best James Bond impression.

Citrus fruits like lemon, lime and orange have so many healing properties. For starters, they're packed with Vitamin C, which your body requires for healthy bones and teeth, and a strong immune system. Vitamin C also helps your body to produce collagen, a protein that has so many important responsibilities, including keeping your skin looking radiant, smooth and youthful. Toss a few extra lime wedges into your water bottle, and toast to that!

Makes 400 ml (13½ fl oz)

2 garlic cloves, finely chopped

2.5 cm (1 in) piece of fresh ginger, peeled and finely chopped

80 ml (2½ fl oz/1/3 cup) freshly squeezed lemon, lime or orange juice (or a combination)

60 ml (2 fl oz/¼ cup) rice-wine vinegar

1 tablespoon maple syrup (optional)

½ bunch coriander (cilantro), roughly chopped

Combine all of your ingredients in a jar, screw the lid on tight and shake vigorously until blended. (Be sure to murmur 'shaken, not stirred' just like Bond, James Bond. Applying to join the British Secret Service is not required...)

Notes

For extra crunch, add some chopped red capsicum (bell pepper).

This dressing is great served on julienned vegetables or in lettuce cups.

DR PAMELA POPPER

Dr Popper is someone I've admired for a long time now. She has written several bestselling books and appeared in some big documentaries too, all while running her own company and leading various campaigns to change laws and national dietary guidelines.

She's a straight-shooter whose depth of knowledge on health and human nutrition makes her a formidable opponent to national health organisations, government agencies, medical professionals, pharmaceutical companies, agricultural organisations and manufacturing companies, many of whom have agendas and priorities that interfere with distributing truthful information and promoting public health.

More than all that, she's an educator who opens eyes, ears and hearts with her unique ability to cut right to the core of an issue.

POTATO MUSHROOM CHOWDER

Potatoes are a staple food in my diet, and soup is one of my favourite ways to eat them in the winter when it's freezing cold in Ohio. I do a lot of batch cooking on Sundays because I don't have much time to cook during the week. This recipe makes a BIG pot of soup, which provides several quick meals during my very busy days. Serves 4-6

1 onion, chopped
220 g (8 oz) button mushrooms, sliced
1.9 litres (64 fl oz) vegetable stock
680 g (1½ lb) waxy potatoes, skin on, cut into bite-sized pieces
4 large carrots, chopped
220 g (8 oz) rotini pasta, cooked according to the packet instructions
2 tablespoons dried oregano
1 tablespoons dried thyme
sea salt and freshly ground black pepper, to taste (optional)

In a large saucepan, sauté the onion and mushroom in a little water until tender.

Add the vegetable stock, potato and carrot, then bring to the boil over a high heat.

Remove 750 ml–1 litre (25½–34 fl oz/3–4 cups) of the stock and vegetables and blend until smooth.

Return the blended soup to the pan, reduce the heat to low and add the cooked pasta, herbs and seasoning.

Cover and simmer for 8–10 minutes, then check and adjust the seasoning if needed.

WHAT ABOUT DEFICIENCIES?
by Andrew

There has never been a recorded case of protein or calcium deficiency in someone eating enough overall calories on a diet of natural, unprocessed foods. A whole food, plant-based diet provides the body with more than enough protein, carbohydrates, fats, vitamins, minerals and fibre. The overwhelming health issue facing today's society is dietary excess. Heart disease, diabetes, obesity and many other chronic diseases are diseases of over consumption rather than deficiency. Big food businesses want to convince us that nutrient X is super important so that we buy more of their product. The meat and dairy industries encourage us to fear protein and calcium deficiencies so that we'll buy their products in ever-increasing amounts. In reality, we have nothing to fear as long as we are eating enough calories from whole, unprocessed plant foods.

ROBYN CHUTER

If you haven't already figured it out, I consider myself a bit of a nerd when it comes to nutrition science, and this is what first attracted me to Robyn Chuter and her work. She's a master of writing long-form articles that leave no stone unturned and really break down the science of an issue. I've nerded out over many of her articles and have since had the privilege to get to know her through a couple of extended, extra-nerdy conversations.

I especially love how Robyn recognises the importance of the psychology behind behavioural change, and understands how futile it can be to attempt major lifestyle changes without understanding exactly what it is that makes them stick.

SWEET POTATO MINT BROWNIES

🍴🍴🍴🍴🍴🍴

I love this recipe because it tastes so rich and decadent, but contains nothing naughty – no oil, sugar or eggs. Not only will it help you meet your daily quota of potatoes and omega-3 fats, but it also contains leafy greens in the form of fresh mint.

It's simple to make, and works well with gluten-free flour mixes. Take this to your next office morning tea, or serve it at your child's birthday party and no one will ever tell you again that you're depriving yourself and your family by eating a whole food, plant-based diet! **Makes 16**

330 g (11½ oz) medjool dates, pitted
10 g (¼ oz/½ cup) fresh mint leaves
200 g (7 oz) steamed sweet potato
60 g (2 oz/½ cup) cacao powder
150 g (5½ oz/1 cup) wholemeal or gluten-free flour
1 teaspoon bicarbonate of soda (baking soda)
1 tablespoon linseed (flaxseed) meal
½ teaspoon peppermint extract or 2 drops peppermint essential oil
Topping
6 medjool dates, pitted
2 tablespoons cacao powder
¼ teaspoon peppermint extract or 1 drop peppermint essential oil
1 ripe banana, peeled

Preheat the oven to 180°C (350°F). Line a 17 x 22 cm (6¾ x 8¾ in) baking tin or Pyrex baking dish with baking paper.

Combine the dates, mint leaves and 250 ml (8½ fl oz/1/ cup) water in a high-speed blender and blitz until puréed. Add the remaining ingredients and pulse until just combined.

Spoon the batter into the prepared baking tin and spread it out evenly.

Bake for 40–45 minutes, or until a toothpick inserted in the middle comes out clean.

While the brownie is baking, prepare the topping. Add all the ingredients to a blender or food processor, adding just enough water to create a spreadable mixture. Blend until smooth, then set aside.

Remove the brownies from the oven and leave to cool. Once cool, turn out of the tin and spread the topping on top.

SHAMIZ AND SHUKUL
HIGH CARB HEALTH

Shamiz and Shukul blew my mind at a talk they gave where they described Shamiz's near-death experience and ultimate recovery from severe ulcerative colitis. They were told that there was no medical cure for his debilitating illness and the only option was to remove part of his colon and take some pretty heavy medication for the rest of his life. At the eleventh hour, Shamiz decided – with help from Shukul – to delay his surgery and try a very strict and specific plant-based eating protocol. What followed was an incredible and inspirational story of recovery to health and fitness that exceeded anything Shamiz's doctors had ever seen.

The brothers were then duty-bound to dedicate their lives to sharing this valuable information with the world and helping others avoid surgery and harmful medication in favour of natural, side effect-free treatments for colitis and other chronic diseases.

'One-quarter of what you eat keeps you alive. The other three-quarters keeps your doctor alive'.

– Ancient Egyptian proverb

POTATOES & CUMIN

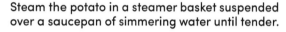

We were both born in India and grew up in New Zealand, so thought it was fitting to create an Indian-style recipe for this incredible book. The recipe is great because it is so simple. If you are worried about what to cook on a plant-based diet, then here is a great example of something fast and easy. This healthy, hearty potato dish is great with a side of roti or naan bread. Serves 4-6

2 kg (4 lb 6 oz) potatoes, peeled and cut into medium chunks
1 teaspoon ground tumeric
1 teaspoon cumin seeds
½ teaspoon asafoetida (hing)
8–10 curry leaves
sea salt, to taste
½ bunch fresh coriander (cilantro), roughly chopped, to garnish (optional)

Steam the potato in a steamer basket suspended over a saucepan of simmering water until tender.

Heat a non-stick frying pan over medium heat and toast the cumin seeds until fragrant. Add a little water, if needed, to stop them from burning.

Add the remaining spices, followed by the steamed potato and mix gently to prevent the potatoes from breaking down.

Season to taste with salt and garnish with fresh coriander.

TIMAREE HAGENBURGER

Figuring out how to make whole food plant-based eating work with a house full of fussy eaters is one of the most common problems I get asked about. Timaree Hagenburger is on a mission to help you solve this problem.

As a registered dietician and nutrition professor, she has the knowledge and skills to help you make it work for everyone. 'The Foodie Bar Way' is her innovative approach to making one meal with many options to satisfy everyone.

She's an avid runner who knows the performance value in plans, having completed several marathons. Her passion lies in education and wellness work, where she is able to connect with those around her and share her knowledge and passion for food, cooking, physical activity and good health.

She blends fun and practicality, as she offers strategies and inspiration for finding pleasure in nourishing meals, because life is better when you 'love the food that loves you back.'

GARLIC ROASTED ROSEMARY POTATOES

Y Y Y Y Y Y

I love using this recipe to prepare potatoes of all sorts – red, purple, golden potatoes and - if you can get your hands on them - purple sweet potatoes. They are crazy delicious! Purple sweet potatoes have less moisture than the sweet potatoes with orange-flesh, so they don't get mushy at all and work super in this recipe! Be sure to leave the skin on all of your spuds, since it doesn't only hold in nutrients, but is packed with them!

Serves 4

5-8 cloves garlic, minced and rested for approximately 10 minutes (see note)
900 g (32 oz) unpeeled purple sweet potatoes, medium diced (see note)
1 tablespoon smoked paprika
1 teaspoon rosemary
1 teaspoon Italian seasoning
juice of 1 large or 2 small lemons
½ teaspoon ground black pepper
more black pepper and salt, to serve

Preheat the oven to 195°C (375°F).

Rest the minced garlic for approximately 10 minutes in a large bowl. Dice the potatoes while you wait.

Add the smoked paprika, rosemary, Italian seasoning and fresh lemon juice to the bowl and stir to form a paste.

Toss the potatoes in the paste to coat. Add lemon juice as needed to avoid the paste becoming too dry.

Transfer to a baking dish and sprinkle with ground black pepper.

Bake, checking and stirring at 35 minutes and then again every 10 minutes until tender.

Season with black pepper and salt.

Notes

Resting the garlic for approximately 10 minutes before putting it in contact with acidic foods/liquids (e.g. lemon juice) or heat maximises its amazing health benefits.

Any variety of potato will work; experiment with different varieties to find your favorites and be sure to try the purple sweet potatoes or any purple potato (packed with the same phytonutrients - anthocyanins - that give blueberries their great reputation!).

CLINT AND MELISSA PADDISON
THE PADDISON PROGRAM

Clint's journey to abundant health started when he was bedridden with intense and constant pain from rheumatoid arthritis. When medications and surgery let him down, Clint turned to his background in science in an effort to take control of his own health. He ultimately arrived at the super anti-inflammatory powers of the whole food, plant-based diet and is now totally pain-free and medication-free, with a beautiful young family to boot!

Clint is part-scientific guru, part-motivational coach and part-health strategist with a giant dose of positive expectation. Melissa loves creating plant-based meals for the family and was instrumental in the discoveries that led to Clint's recovery. Clint reflects that until he took responsibility for his own destiny, he'd been 'outsourcing' his health problems for other people to deal with. He now spends his time writing, speaking and coaching others in how they can experience the same astounding results that he's had.

PASTA & POTATO FAGIOLI

ŤŤŤŤŤŤ

This recipe is a family favourite and one that has been enjoyed since Melissa's childhood, when she would cook Sunday dinners with her Italian grandmother. This was a staple meal that everyone loved and knew as 'Grandma's Specialty', as it was good for our bellies and food for our hearts. When we created The Paddison Program, it was a meal that Melissa knew she wanted to adapt and include, as it is wholesome, filling and one that the whole family can enjoy. This hearty soup is still a favourite for our plant-based family. **Serves 2**

1 onion, diced
2 garlic cloves, minced
2 medium carrots, diced
3 celery stalks and leaves, diced
3 teaspoons dried Italian herbs
2 bay leaves
750 ml (25½ fl oz/3 cups) vegetable stock
2 white potatoes, diced
2 x 400 g (14 oz) tins cannellini beans, drained and rinsed
1 x 800 g (28 oz) tin crushed tomatoes
90 g (3 oz/1 cup) ditalini pasta
sea salt, to taste
chilli flakes, to taste
1 bunch flat-leaf (Italian) parsley, roughly chopped
green salad and sourdough bread, to serve (optional)

Add the onion, garlic, carrot and celery to a large stockpot with the Italian herbs and bay leaves. Add a little of the vegetable stock and simmer over a low heat for 2 minutes.

Add the potato, cannellini beans, crushed tomatoes, remaining vegetable stock and 250 ml (8½ fl oz/1 cup) water. Mix well, then simmer over a medium heat for approximately 20 minutes, or until the potatoes have softened.

Bring a separate small saucepan of water to the boil and cook the pasta according to the packet instructions. Drain, and add to the stockpot.

Season with salt and chilli flakes. Serve garnished with the parsley and alongside a fresh green salad and a slice of sourdough bread, if desired.

DR CONOR KERLEY

After being diagnosed with multiple sclerosis at the ripe old age of 15, Dr Kerley turned to nutrition in an effort to free himself from this debilitating illness.This had a huge impact on his life and led him to study human nutrition and dietetics at Trinity College, Dublin.

He went on to achieve a PhD and publish over 20 peer-reviewed scientific studies. He is now an internationally known dietitian, lecturing on plant-based health with a special interest in autoimmune and heart and lung diseases.

POTATO & LEEK SOUP

I, like most of Ireland and our ancestors, love potatoes; they are so nutritious and versatile. Potatoes are available worldwide and they're cheap, making them an easy staple to incorporate into a delicious meal. Potato and leek soup is very popular in Ireland, where I'm from, but it is often loaded with butter and cream. However, it's possible to make hearty soups without the addition of heavy animal-based products. You can also pack them full of a variety of other healthy ingredients. And you needn't follow an exact recipe to make this, or any other, soup; just work with what fresh vegetables you have and what you're in the mood for.

A pressure cooker is a useful bit of equipment to have in your kitchen, and it makes this simple soup even quicker to make. Try adding some more substantial ingredients, such as lentils or pearl barley, if you want to make this soup even more filling. **Serves 4**

1.5–2 litres (51–68 fl oz/6–8 cups) vegetable stock
2 onions, roughly chopped
2–4 garlic cloves
1 large leek, trimmed and roughly chopped
(make sure you wash or soak it to remove any soil or grit)
3 potatoes, roughly chopped (skin on or off – your choice)
1 bouquet garni
freshly ground black pepper

Heat the vegetable stock in a large stockpot over a medium–high heat.

Heat another stockpot or large saucepan over a medium heat, add the onions and garlic and a ladle of the stock and sweat for 1–2 minutes. Add the leek and fry for 1–2 minutes, then add the potatoes, bouquet garni and hot vegetable stock and bring to the boil over a high heat.

Cover with a lid, reduce the heat to medium–low and simmer for 10–15 minutes until the potatoes have softened. Season to taste with pepper and any other spices of your choice.

Take the pot off the heat and remove the bouquet garni. Blend with a hand-held blender until very smooth.

CYRUS KHAMBATTA, PHD & ROBBY BARBARO
MASTERING DIABETES

Cyrus and Robby both live and thrive with type-1 diabetes. Unlike type-2, type-1 diabetes can't be completely cured, however they have had great success in managing their blood glucose and achieving amazing metabolic health in the process.

From the first time we spoke, it's been easy for me to see that these two don't let diabetes get them down; on the contrary, Cyrus says that having diabetes is the best thing that ever happened to him, as it has given him motivation to attack life with all he's got.

They talk the talk; Cyrus holds a PhD in Nutritional Biochemistry while Robby is studying towards a Masters in Public Health. They also walk the walk, leading by example to show people with diabetes what is possible. Together, they run 'Mastering Diabetes', a program where they coach and educate people on reversing insulin resistance with plant-based nutrition.

SWEET POTATOES LOADED W LENTIL STEW

Legumes (beans, peas, and lentils) have an exceptionally low glycemic index, so adding them to any meal helps to slow the rate at which the glucose of the meal is absorbed into the bloodstream. They even have what is called the 'second meal effect', meaning that the beneficial effects of beans for blood glucose control last hours beyond the meal in which they were eaten (or even into the next day). So this sweet potato and lentil stew recipe will not only taste amazing, but you'll have steady numbers all day after you eat it. Does it get any better than that?! **Serves 3–4**

3 sweet potatoes (any variety: Garnett, purple, Japanese, Hawaiian, etc.)
185 g (6½ oz/1 cup) green or brown lentils, rinsed
1 large red onion, finely chopped
3 celery stalks, finely chopped
2 large carrots, finely chopped
4–6 garlic cloves, finely chopped
90 g (3 oz/1 cup) sliced mushrooms
180 g (6½ oz/1 cup) sliced cherry tomatoes
7 g (¼ oz/¼ cup) fresh rosemary leaves
10 g (¼ oz/¼ cup) fresh thyme leaves
2–3 cups silverbeet (Swiss chard), chopped
juice of 1 lemon

Preheat the oven to 180°C (350°F).

Pierce the potatoes a few times with a fork, place on a baking tray lined with baking paper and bake for 1 hour, or until the flesh is tender and easily pierced with a sharp knife.

In a stockpot, combine the lentils, onion, celery, carrot and garlic with 1 litre (34 fl oz/4 cups) water. Bring to the boil over a high heat, then reduce the heat and simmer for about 30 minutes.

Add the mushrooms, tomatoes and herbs and simmer another 7–10 minutes.

Check that the lentils are soft, then remove from heat. Stir in the silverbeet and lemon juice and leave to wilt for a few minutes.

Slice the sweet potatoes in half lengthways and spoon a generous helping of lentil stew on top.

DR DOUG LISLE

On the surface my Spud Fit Challenge seemed to most like a shallow, short-sighted attempt at weight loss and health, with 15 minutes of fame on the side. At its core it was a total overhaul of my psychological wellbeing, beginning with my relationship with food.

Shortly after I started I was recommended a book that quickly became my favourite of all time: 'The Pleasure Trap', by Dr Doug Lisle and Dr Alan Goldhamer - a mind-bending, paradigm-busting book that taught me an incredible amount about health and food psychology and gave me great confidence that I was walking the right path.

Dr Doug Lisle is a pioneering psychologist with revolutionary ideas on self-esteem and wellbeing. He describes his approach as 'Esteem Dynamics', its core insights adapted from the theory of evolution and applied as a biological approach to psychology. He understands better than anyone the way food affects our psychological state and how we can adjust our mindset and behaviour to get the best out of life. His approach to the difficulties faced by modern humans is so utterly logical, simple and reasonable that whenever he talks I'm constantly amazed that I haven't already got it all figured out!

THE PLEASURE TRAP

If getting healthy were just a matter of getting the right information, then it would be a fairly simple task. The right information is now readily available and has been presented by some great educators – people like T. Colin Campbell, John McDougall (see page 19), Caldwell Esselstyn, Jr., Dean Ornish and Neal Barnard, among many others. However, the message has been met with serious resistance on multiple levels, and it is not simple to get past this resistance.

The most obvious level of resistance operates at an economic-political level. Big Food, Big Pharma, and big government forces push the truth as far away from people as possible, because no one makes any easy money when healthy people eat simple, healthful foods and take no pills. It is no surprise, then, that the honest consumer today is quite confused. Despite this engineered confusion, a few fortunate people still find their way to the truth. If you are holding this book, then you are one of those people.

However, once we get to the truth – to seeing the health-protecting and health-restoring power of a natural-foods diet – there is still great resistance. This time, the resistance is not from governments and corporations, but, in startling contrast, from us.

That resistance is the result of an ancient instinct that guided our ancestors towards survival in an environment of food scarcity. Our ancestors were designed to relentlessly seek the most efficient methods for obtaining precious caloric energy. In order to do this most effectively, they evolved taste preferences for foods that contain concentrated calories, and evolved pleasure mechanisms that are responsive to calorie density. This is why corn is tastier than lettuce; it has more calories per pound. In the modern world, humans would learn to tear apart their food and reconstitute it, putting it back together with just the rich pieces. Ice cream, chocolate, oil and cheeseburgers would become typical of the new 'food' – food with calorie densities much greater than anything that exists in the natural world.

Inside each of us is this instinct – a preference for foods with the highest calorie densities. This super-stoking of the pleasure instinct leads the unwary directly into a trap where the diet is overly rich, the person is overfed and an entire civilization suffers from diseases almost exclusively caused by dietary excess. We call this motivational confusion 'the pleasure trap'.

Books such as this – with information about what to do, but also how to do it – are essential. Try a recipe. Then try another. And then another. Build for yourself a simple but excellent array of choices that you can enjoy again and again. Simplicity and repetition are the keys to successfully escaping the pleasure trap. Use this guidebook, and you will find – and keep – the life you deserve.

Douglas J. Lisle, PhD, co-author of 'The Pleasure Trap: Mastering the Hidden Force that Undermines Health and Happiness'

ATHLETES

No one embodies what a plant-based diet can do for you better than an athlete. Collectively, they represent to me the true essence of what it is to be human. The people in this chapter are at their physical peak, and understand that there is so much more to it than just training hard. A Ferrari is worth nothing if it's running on dirty fuel, and these people have certainly nailed down the best way to get their engines to fire on all cylinders.

Society has an unhealthy obsession with animal protein. It seems like everyone is smashing down steaks and gulping down shakes in an attempt to become as strong as an ox, forgetting that an ox eats grass. These phenomenal athletes show us in no uncertain terms that animal protein is a thing of the past. If we want to put premium fuel in our Ferraris, then we need to get it from plants. Read on to see how potatoes help these performance machines to prepare, perform and recover.

MORGAN MITCHELL

Morgan Mitchell is a multiple Australian champion and Olympian in the 400 m sprint. She's the embodiment of power, speed and grace, and she does it all fuelled by plants. Need I say more?

Morgan is equally impressive off the track; she's positively effervescent and you can't help but feel buoyed in her presence. Having been questioned and doubted about her transition to a plant-based lifestyle, she made the semi-finals at the 2016 Rio Olympics and moved to eighth place on the Australian 400 m all-time list. She competes in one of the toughest sports in the world and in one of the toughest events with her trademark positivity intact.

Using her profile to share the benefits of a plant-based diet, she has inspired countless young athletes to broaden their minds to the possibilities of plant-based eating.

AIR—FRIED POTATO FRIES

I got this recipe from my coach's sister. I love spicy food and I love fries. They are also healthier than regular fries and easy to make, so I don't feel the least bit guilty when I have them. Serves 2

3 medium white potatoes
Seasoning
½ teaspoon each of sea salt and freshly ground black pepper
½ teaspoon vegetable stock powder
¼ teaspoon paprika
¼ teaspoon cayenne pepper
1 teaspoon all-purpose seasoning

Peel and cut the potatoes into fries (the size doesn't matter – just make sure they're even). Place them in a bowl, cover with cold water and leave to soak for 30 minutes.

Preheat an air-fryer to 180°C (350°F).

Drain the potatoes and rinse well, then dry with paper towels, removing as much moisture as possible.

For the seasoning, combine all the ingredients in a large bowl and set aside.

Place half of the potatoes in the fryer basket and insert into the air fryer. Cook for 5 minutes, then increase the temperature to 200°C (400°F). Pull the basket out and, using tongs, toss and stir the potatoes. Return the basket to the fryer and continue cooking until the potatoes are cooked through and golden brown on the outside, about another 15 minutes, opening the basket two or three times during cooking to toss and stir them.

Transfer the potatoes to the bowl with the seasoning and toss to coat evenly. Return the fryer temperature to 180°C (350°F) and repeat with the remaining potatoes. Serve immediately.

DISCIPLINE
by Andrew

The process required to get results from our diet is very similar to the way we approach training: consistency is key! If you keep showing up, day after day, week after week and month after month to consistently put together a solid training program, then it is unavoidable that you will develop your fitness to a higher level. If you skip the odd session here and there and don't give all you've got in some other sessions, then results will come more slowly. Our approach to diet should be no different; we can't expect to be at our best if we throw regular cheat days into the mix. When it comes to our health, 'near enough is good enough' just doesn't cut the mustard!

AMANDA ROSE

I turned on the TV one afternoon just in time to see a story on a fitness competitor who'd lost a ton of weight and got in the best shape of her life by following a whole food, plant-based diet and eating a heap of, wait for it... potatoes! Amanda Rose is a self-confessed carboholic who was an overweight junk-food vegetarian before transitioning to a whole food, potato-based diet in 2010. She suffered with rheumatoid arthritis, acne and low energy for a long time, while struggling against her love of high-carb foods, which lead her to being 22 kg (50 lb) overweight.

Everything changed when she discovered that whole, unprocessed foods rich in carbohydrates weren't to blame! Now she eats all the delicious carbs she wants and has no trouble staying in shape. She also specialises in helping women become 'plant-based babes' and unlock their full potential with the power of carbs.

MEXICAN SMOKY LOADED FRIES

⫮⫮⫮⫮⫮⫮

I love chips! If I could live off only two meals for the rest of my life, it would be chips and smoothie bowls, no joke. I love this recipe because it combines a smoky barbecue flavour with Mexican flare. It's also low in fat and high-carb: the perfect combination.
Serves 1

Smoked pulled jackfruit:
200 g (7 oz) tinned jackfruit, drained
2 teaspoons tomato paste (concentrated purée)
1 teaspoon apple-cider vinegar
1 teaspoon liquid smoke (for an extra-smoky flavour) (optional)
¼ capsicum (bell pepper), diced
pinch each of smoked paprika, black pepper, cayenne, sea salt and cumin
Chips:
300 g (10½ oz) potatoes, peeled and cut into chips
1 tablespoon sea salt
Green drizzle:
½ avocado
25 g (1 oz/½ cup) baby spinach
pinch of cracked black pepper
60 ml (2 fl oz/¼ cup) water
Pico de gallo:
½ tomato, diced
1 tablespoon diced red onion
juice of ¼ lime
½ teaspoon ground coriander
Topping:
1 tablespoon nutritional yeast
1 tablespoon chopped coriander (cilantro)
1 tablespoon chopped spring onion (scallion)
sliced jalapeño chilli (optional)
1 tablespoon fresh, raw corn kernels (optional)

Preheat the oven to 220°C (430°F).

Combine all the ingredients for the smoked pulled jackfruit in a Crock-pot (slow cooker) and cook on stew mode for 45 minutes.

Put the potato chips on a baking tray lined with baking paper and season with the salt. Bake for 20–30 minutes, until browned and crispy. Remove and keep warm.

To prepare the green drizzle, combine all the ingredients in a blender and blitz until smooth. Set aside.

Mix all of the pico de gallo ingredients in a small bowl.

When the jackfruit is tender, pull it apart with two forks to create the 'pulled' texture.

Layer the chips, jackfruit and pico de gallo on a serving plate and top with the green drizzle, nutritional yeast, coriander and spring onion. Add the jalapeño chilli and corn kernels, if using.

CRISSI CARVALHO
VEGAN FITNESS MODEL

Crissi is recognised in body-building circles the world over as the 'Vegan Fitness Model'. As a fully plant-powered athlete at 45 years of age, she still mixes it up with athletes half her age and shows no sign of slowing down any time soon. She initially went plant-based in an effort to treat her own ill-health, and it paid off. So effective was this strategy that, before long, she was feeling so energised that she made a comeback to competition after a 20-year absence!

She has since competed in dozens of events all over the world and spends her time coaching women to create a healthier, leaner lifestyle with the power of whole foods. For me, the most impressive thing is the way she empowers women to work hard on their health and fitness, while also embracing and changing the way they see their perceived flaws and imperfections.

GERMAN KARTOFFEL POTATO MUSCLE PANCAKES

These amazing German potato cakes are a vegan, whole food, higher-protein version of the popular and a traditional German dish, Kartoffel pfannkuchen, AKA Potato pancakes. I decided to bake them, not fry, reducing the need for oil, with added silken/soft tofu making this dish a macro-balanced treat! Either top with warmed apple sauce, or get more savoury with mushrooms, nutritional yeast, or top it with warm rhubarb or berry compote.

A dish you can have for breakfast, lunch, a snack, dinner or dessert! Makes 6-8 pancakes

1kg (2 lb 3 oz) white potatoes, grated
1 carrot, grated
1 onion, finely chopped
225 g (8 oz/1 cup) silken tofu (or medium tofu)
125 ml (4 fl oz/½ cup) apple sauce
3 tablespoons chia seeds
1 tablespoon ground linseeds, flaxseeds or hemp seeds
½ teaspoon sea salt
½ teaspoon freshly ground black pepper
your choice of toppings, such as more apple sauce,
nutritional yeast, berries, sauerkraut or stewed rhubarb

Preheat the oven to 180°C (350°F). Line a baking tray with baking paper.

Combine the potato, carrot and onion in a large bowl and mix well.

Combine the tofu, apple sauce, chia seeds and linseeds in a blender and blitz to a smooth consistency. Add to the bowl with the potato mixture, along with the salt and pepper, and mix until well combined.

Scoop equal amounts of the mixture (about two-thirds of a cup) at a time onto the baking tray and flatten slightly to create potato 'cakes'. Each cake should be about 1 cm (½ in) thick.

Bake for 15 minutes, then turn and continue baking for another 15 minutes until brown.

Serve with your choice of toppings. OMG – ich liebe es!

EILEEN AND GILIAN REICHERT
OM TWIINS

The Om Twiins will have you buzzing with excitement and ready to move mountains on the road to fitness and health. They originally went vegan after learning from and being inspired by some powerful activists online. They watched some incredible speeches and some eye-opening undercover videos. It was a daunting move at first, because neither of them had ever met another vegan! As personal fitness trainers, they quickly learned about the performance benefits and saw great results in their own training and fitness levels, which further cemented to them that they'd made the right choice.

They now combine the benefits of eating whole plants with their passion for fitness to help others become cruelty-free athletes. Eileen and Gilian are powerful women who back up their words with action and determination, but also understand the importance of enjoying what they do. They love to have fun and share their passion with those who they train.

TROPICAL FUEL SMOOTHIE

One of our favourite ingredients for any smoothie is sweet potatoes. Why?:
1. They are loaded with healthy carbs and other essential nutrients, making any smoothie a perfect meal before and after a killer workout.
2. They give a smooth, creamy texture.
3. They are one of the cheapest, most accessible foods in the world – any type will work. Serves 1

1 large, ripe banana, peeled (freeze for a creamier texture)
150 g (5½ oz) fresh or frozen mango, sliced
100 g (3½ oz) sweet potato, cut into chunks, boiled and cooled
250 ml (8½ fl oz/1 cup) plant-based milk of your choice
1 tablespoon chia seeds
handful of ice cubes

Combine all the ingredients in a high-speed blender and blitz for 2 minutes until smooth.

JOEL KIRKILIS

I first heard of Joel when I saw him posing on the front of a magazine in a top that said 'I love tofu!' It turned out that he was a vegan bodybuilder at the top of his game and doing big things in competitions. Even though I was already vegan at the time, I didn't know of any athletes like him and was amazed to see the physique that he had built without any need for animal products – I was an instant fan!

Joel is as much an activist as he is an athlete, leading by example to show what's possible with plants, and opening hearts and minds along the way. Through bodybuilding and CrossFit, he proves that insane levels of strength and fitness can been achieved, and that it can be done without hurting animals in the process. When we started out, vegan athletes were few and far between, and he is inspired to see how far the movement has come and how many amazing vegan athletes are around these days. I bet a good number of them went down this road by following his lead.

POTATO SALAD

ŤŤŤŤŤŤ

This is a tasty recipe that I have enjoyed eating since I was a child. It is incredibly simple to make, looks vibrant and is nutritious and filling. The original recipe uses mayonnaise, however I have replaced it with a low-fat, vegan version that is as creamy and satisfying as the original. Serves 2

500 g (1 lb 2 oz) brushed potatoes
250 g (9 oz) carrots, chopped
100 g (3½ oz) green beans, whole
50 g (1¾ oz) fresh peas
2 tablespoons home-made mayonnaise (see below)
2 small dill sprigs, roughly chopped
sea salt and freshly ground black pepper, to taste
Home-made mayonnaise
125 ml (4 fl oz/½ cup) aquafaba (see breakout box, right)
½ teaspoon mustard
2 teaspoons apple-cider vinegar
pinch of sea salt

Put the potatoes in a large saucepan, cover with cold water and bring to the boil over a high heat. Reduce the heat to low and simmer until tender and the flesh is easily pierced with a sharp knife. Remove from the water and leave to cool.

Add the carrots to the boiling water and cook for 3 minutes, or until tender, then add the green beans and peas and cook for another 1 minute until soft. Drain and transfer to a serving bowl.

To make the mayonnaise, simply combine all the ingredients in a small bowl and set aside.

Once the potatoes have cooled, dice into small cubes and combine with the other vegetables.

Add the mayonnaise and season to taste with salt and pepper, then stir again until the potatoes are evenly coated. Sprinkle with the chopped dill.

AQUAFABA
by Mandy

Aquafaba literally means water-bean, and is the leftover water from cooking beans. It is amazing stuff! Because of its emulsifying, foaming, binding, gelatinising and thickening qualities, it is mostly used as a much healthier alternative to eggs. This makes it a very useful addition to a whole food, plant-based diet. Use it to thicken sauces and as a base for dressings. It also makes a delicious mayonnaise! The best aquafaba tends to be from chickpeas, and the easiest way to obtain it in a reliable consistency is to use the chickpea water from a drained tin of chickpeas.

Side note: aquafaba is also (and most famously) used for evil too: paired with a heap of sugar and whipped for long enough, it will eventually form a meringue. I take no responsibility for how you use (or misuse) that information!

LUKE AND EMILIE TAN

A few years ago, I went to a powerlifting workshop and was in awe of the strength shown by Luke. Later I learned more about his battles with mental health and his progression from an overweight kid to an elite athlete, which took his story to a new level for me. Emilie is a certified raw-food chef and an elite ultra-runner who has won multiple championships and represented her country with distinction. Together, they are a dynamic duo who are way too high achieving to be friends with me! On top of their own personal achievements, they somehow find the time to coach others and promote the plant-based lifestyle through educational initiatives like the 'Plant Fit Summit'.

INDIAN SHEPHERD'S PIE

This is one of our favourite recipes as it's rich in complex carbohydrates and plant-based protein to fuel our athletic endeavours. Emilie is from Quebec and we are now based in Singapore, so this dish is a plant-based variation of Pâté Chinois (Quebec shepherd's pie). Serves 3-4

600–700 g (1 lb 5 oz–1 lb 9 oz) sweet potatoes, peeled and cut into chunks
170 ml (5½ fl oz/⅔ cup) plant-based milk of your choice
1 medium onion, chopped
4 garlic cloves, minced
250–300 g (9–10½ oz) button mushrooms, chopped
250 ml (8½ fl oz/1 cup) crushed tomatoes
2 teaspoons Indian curry powder
400 g (14 oz/2 cups) cooked brown lentils
155 g (5½ oz/1 cup) frozen mixed peas and corn
30 g (1 oz/¼ cup) chopped spring onions (scallions), to garnish (optional)
sprinkle of cayenne pepper (optional)

Preheat the oven to 190°C (375°F).

Put the sweet potatoes and a pinch of salt in a large saucepan, cover with cold water and bring to the boil over a high heat. Cook for about 10 minutes, then drain and return the potatoes to the pan to dry out. Add the plant milk and another pinch of salt and mash well. Set aside.

Set a large saucepan over a medium heat and stir-fry the onion and garlic in a splash of water for a few minutes until the onions are translucent, then increase the heat to high and add the mushrooms. Fry until the mushrooms become soft and start to brown.

Add the tomatoes and curry powder. Stir well, then add the cooked lentils, peas and corn. Simmer for another minute or two, then taste and adjust the seasoning with more curry powder and salt as necessary.

Transfer the lentil mixture to a 20 cm (8 in) baking dish, spreading it out in an even, flat layer. Cover with the mashed potatoes and use a fork to run lines across the top in an even layer.

Bake for about 25 minutes and serve as is or garnished with the spring onions and cayenne pepper, if using.

AMANDA MEGGISON

Amanda is a huge inspiration to me. She has stared down some of Australia's toughest endurance challenges without taking a backwards step. She is tough, fearless and relentless in sport and in life.

She's a trailblazer who proves that no matter how busy and active you are, following a plant-based diet is the ideal nutrition plan and philosophy to power your life. It's more than that though, it's about harnessing the inherent life force in plants and thriving on their positive energy. This is reflected in her work as a nutrition and running coach through Planted Life.

Amanda's philosophy is simple: MIND | BODY | FOOD. Adopting mindfulness and awareness when it comes to your lifestyle choices will help contribute towards a healthy mindset, including a healthy body image. Together, we can simplify our food choices, having nothing but a positive impact on our bodies and minds.

GNOCCHI W̲ A BASIC TOMATO SAUCE

♈ ♈ ♈ ♈ ♈ ♈

When it comes to fuelling for an endurance event, we 'carb load' not 'garb load', as it is imperative that we pay attention to our body's nutritional needs 100 per cent of the time. After all, you get out what you put in. These gnocchi and curry recipes were designed for the time-poor and health conscious. Using simple and tasty ingredients to complement the humble spud, the vegetables are the main stars in these recipes, never playing the supporting role.

Serves 2–3

Gnocchi
2–3 medium white potatoes
1 teaspoon sea salt
1 tablespoon nutritional yeast
150 g (5½ oz/1 cup) organic plain (all-purpose) flour, plus extra for dusting
Tomato sauce
1 x 400 g (14 oz) tin whole tomatoes
sea salt and freshly ground black pepper, to taste
2 tablespoons chopped fresh herbs, such as basil and flat-leaf (Italian) parsley (optional)

To make the gnocchi, wash the potatoes (leaving the skins on), place in a large saucepan and cover with cold water. Bring to the boil over a high heat and cook for 30 minutes, or until the flesh is easily pierced with a knife and the skins start to break away.

Drain, and leave to cool.

To prepare the sauce, add the tomatoes to a saucepan and blend them with a hand-held blender until smooth. Season with salt and pepper, and add the herbs, if using. Set aside until ready to serve.

Once the potatoes are cool enough to handle, scoop the flesh out into a large bowl. Using a potato ricer or masher, mash the potatoes until smooth.

Add the salt, savoury yeast flakes and, bit by bit, the flour to the potato mixture until it forms a soft dough. If the dough is a little dry, add 1–2 tablespoons water.

Use your hands to roll out the dough on a floured surface into a 1 cm (½ in) thick log. Slice the log into 2.5 cm (1 in) pieces and transfer to a floured plate or bowl. Dust well with the flour to make sure they don't stick to each other.

Bring a large saucepan of water to the boil.

Carefully add the gnocchi, in batches if necessary, being careful not to overcrowd the pan. The gnocchi will sink to the bottom at first. When they begin to float – about 2–3 minutes – the gnocchi are cooked. Remove them with a slotted spoon and place in a large baking dish. Repeat until all the gnocchi are cooked. While cooking your gnocchi, gently reheat the tomato sauce until hot.

Serve immediately with the tomato sauce.

POTATO & TOMATO CURRY

Serves 2

1 teaspoon yellow mustard seeds
4 fresh curry leaves, plus extra to serve
½ brown onion, quartered
1 teaspoon ground coriander
1 teaspoon ground cumin
½ teaspoon ground turmeric
¼ teaspoon chilli powder
2 Roma tomatoes, quartered and
 deseeded
1 large potato, peeled and cubed
125 ml (4 fl oz/½ cup) tomato juice

Heat 60 ml (2 fl oz/¼ cup) water in a
large saucepan. Add the mustard seeds,
curry leaves and onion and stir-fry over a
medium heat until the onions are soft and
translucent.

Stir in the spices and tomatoes and cook for
1–3 minutes. If the mixture becomes dry, add
a splash of water and continue to stir.

Add the potato and tomato juice to the
saucepan, reduce the heat to low and
simmer for 20–30 minutes until the potatoes
are tender. If the mixture dried out too much,
add up to another 60 ml (2 fl oz/¼ cup)
water.

Serve hot, garnished with fresh curry leaves.

GOAL SETTING

by Andrew

Most athletes are particularly keen goal setters, just like those of us who want to lose weight. We set numbers for ourselves that we need to achieve, or events that we need to be in perfect shape for. We put immense pressure on ourselves to achieve these (often unrealistic) goals, and we attach our own sense of worth to them. When the inevitable failure comes, often our self-esteem comes crashing down with it and we spiral into cycles of depression and self-destructive behaviour.

Our society is so focused on achievements and results that we've forgotten all about what gets us there in the first place: hard work. No amount of focus alone can help us reach our goals. No amount of concentration on a number can help it appear in front of your marathon time or, for that matter, on your scales. Wanting, believing, positive self-talk and planning can do nothing to help bring us closer to our goals either. All highly successful people understand is that ACTION is the only thing that is important, and it is the only thing that can have any real effect on our success (or lack thereof) in reaching our goals.

Our goals should therefore reflect the importance of actions. It's fine to say 'I want to run a three-hour marathon' or 'I want to lose 100 kg', but the far more important goal is what you are going to do about it today. We don't have ultimate control over numbers. We can influence them with our actions, but we can't decide what they will be. However we do have ultimate control over what our actions will be. We can decide what we will eat and drink, how far and at what intensity we will run, and how much sleep we get (unless we have a newborn baby, as I have at the time of writing this book!).

The only good reason I can think of for setting a long-term goal is that it can help us decide what our actions should be today. If you want to run a three-hour marathon or lose weight next year, what do you need to do today to set that in motion? Set a goal and then forget about the end result and focus on the next thing you have to do to get closer to it. When your actions are in alignment with your goal, then it just makes sense that you will move closer to it. When you get the process right, then success becomes inevitable. It also makes it feel more possible to achieve a large, long-term goal if you tackle it in bite-sized chunks.

This new method also changes the way that we track our progress. No matter what we do, we will have days, weeks and even months where the numbers tell us that we are not getting closer to our ultimate goal. If those numbers are all we have, then it can be easy to get discouraged and throw in the towel. For this reason, it is important that we track other, more important aspects of our progress. The famous basketball coach John Wooden said that 'success is the satisfaction you get from knowing you did your job properly'. If an athlete can look at a training diary and know that they have completed each and every one of their training sessions to the best of their ability, then they can take great pride and satisfaction from that. They can also rest assured that it's a matter of time until they smash through their plateau. The same can be said for weight loss and health: focus on what you eat and you will see the scales move on their own.

Give yourself a tick on the calendar for every day where your actions and behaviours were perfect. Aim to string as many of those days as you can together and, after a month or even a week of perfect behaviour and action, you will see your goals drawing nearer. After a year, you won't even recognise the person looking back at you in the mirror.

MIKE CASE
VEGAINZ

Mike is the gorilla behind 'Vegainz Coach'. Contrary to the typical meat-heavy approach of most strength-based athletes, Mike switched to the 'plant life' in an effort to seek a health and performance advantage. He quickly noticed impressive gains in his strength, energy, clarity and recovery, and hasn't looked back since. He's now a strength and body transformation coach who is hell-bent on seeing the herbivores of the world take advantage of all the Vegainz. You only have to spend 2 minutes with Mike to see that his energy is high and his passion for life and strength is overflowing. The first step on your path to becoming a plant-based gorilla is by eating his spud and bean burgers!

SPUD + BEAN BURGERS W SPICY BARBECUE PEACH SAUCE

Never again will you be lost for words when someone asks you, but what do you eat when you have a barbecue? I have the perfect addition to any barbecue gathering that will impress the masses, carnivores and veggies alike! I like to stuff these burgers in a good-quality sourdough bun, add a dollop of peach sauce, coconut yoghurt, onions and some leafy greens. EPIC!
Serves 4-6

Peach sauce
6 yellow peaches
4 spring onions (scallions), finely sliced
2 garlic cloves, minced
2½ tablespoons apple-cider vinegar
60 g (2 oz/⅓ cup) coconut sugar
pinch of chilli flakes
2 teaspoons Dijon mustard
leaves from 12 thyme sprigs
½ teaspoon each of sea salt and freshly
 ground black pepper
Burgers
230 g (8 oz/1 cup) boiled, smashed spuds
185 g (6½ oz/1 cup) organic firm tofu
1 small red onion, diced
90 g (3 oz/½ cup) brown-rice flour
pinch of chilli flakes
2½ teaspoons smoked paprika, plus extra to
 serve
2 teaspoons maple syrup (optional)
1 teaspoon soy sauce or tamari
sea salt and freshly ground black pepper, to
 taste 130 g (4½ oz/¾ cup) cooked black beans
185 g (6½ oz/1 cup) cooked brown rice
lettuce and other salad toppings, to serve
1 teaspoon coconut yoghurt per burger, to
 serve

To make the peach sauce, place the peaches in a saucepan of boiling water and leave them to sit for up to 2 minutes. Drain, then leave to cool slightly before sliding the skins off and cutting the flesh into small chunks.

Set a saucepan over a medium heat and add the spring onions and garlic with a splash of water. Fry for 2 minutes, or until softened.

Add the remaining ingredients and continue cooking over a medium heat until the sauce begins to boil. Reduce the heat to low and cook for up to another 10 minutes, stirring occasionally to ensure the sauce doesn't burn. Remove from the heat and set aside.

For the burgers, add all the ingredients, except one-third of the black beans and the rice, to a food processor and blend until well combined. Scrape the mixture into a mixing bowl and add the remaining black beans and brown rice.

Preheat the oven to 200°C (400°F).

Shape the mixture into burgers and place on a baking tray lined with baking paper. Flatten the patties slightly with your hand to your desired thickness. I slightly separate my fingers to create indents, similar to what you get when you grill burgers on a barbecue.

Bake for approximately 20 minutes, turning the burgers halfway through. Remove and leave to cool for a few minutes before serving.

Assemble your burger in whatever order you like. Lettuce doesn't have to go on the bottom. In fact, use any type of leafy green you desire. Have fun building your own burger with salad toppings but, whatever you do, don't forget a big lashing of the peach sauce mixed with some coconut yoghurt and an extra sprinkle of smoked paprika. YUM!

SIMON HILL
PLANTPROOF

Formerly one of Australia's most successful entrepreneurs, Simon's energy is, these days, directed towards giving people the knowledge and confidence to make informed decisions around their diet and health. Before making the change himself, Simon had all the same fear, trepidations and questions that everyone has: 'Am I going to lose muscle?', 'Will I gain fat and feel bloated?', 'What about my iron?', 'Will I get enough protein?'

Simon went deep down the rabbit hole of nutrition research, sought advice from others who'd been there and done it, and ultimately took the plunge himself and learned from his own experience too. These days, he runs 'Plant Proof', a free educational hub for plant-based eaters and the plant-curious. The answers to the health issues of society can't be found in a medicine cabinet. Living closer to nature is the only path to true health and Simon wants to help you get there.

SWEET POTATO + BLACK BEAN TEMPEH TACOS ᵂ CASHEW CHEESE SAUCE SAUCE

⑂⑂⑂⑂⑂⑂⑂

The mildly spiced sweet potato combines perfectly with the protein-dense, black bean tempeh to create a super-healthy take on an otherwise traditional Mexican recipe. Absolutely oozing with flavour, I have no doubt in my mind that this will become your new go-to recipe for Taco Tuesday. Perfect for all ages! Serves 4-6

Taco filling
1 medium sweet potato
1 small onion, finely chopped
2–3 garlic cloves, minced
1 jalapeño, finely chopped
300 g (10½ oz) black bean tempeh (or soy tempeh or 300 g/10½ oz cooked black beans)
1½ teaspoons chilli flakes
1 teaspoon ground cumin
½ teaspoon ground turmeric
½ teaspoon ground paprika, plus extra for seasoning
1 bunch kale, finely chopped
big pinch of sea salt
freshly ground black pepper, to taste
kernels from 1 large corn cob
Cashew cheese sauce
155 g (5½ oz/1 cup) raw cashew nuts, soaked overnight
1 tablespoon lime juice
15 g (0.5 oz/¼ cup) nutritional yeast
¼ teaspoon sea salt
½ teaspoon ground cumin
½ teaspoon cayenne pepper
½ teaspoon ground turmeric
¼ teaspoon garlic powder
To serve:
corn tortillas, warmed
thinly sliced cabbage
sliced avocado
lime wedges
salsa
chopped coriander (cilantro)

Preheat the oven to 220°C (430°F).

Wrap the sweet potato in foil, making small holes in the foil so the potato can breathe. Bake for 45 minutes to 1 hour until tender and the flesh is easily pierced with a sharp knife.

For the cashew cheese sauce, drain the water from the cashews and place them in a high-speed blender. Add the lemon juice, nutritional yeast, salt, spices and 185 ml (6 fl oz/¾ cup) water. Blend on high speed for 1–2 minutes, or until smooth.

If you prefer a thicker cashew-cheese texture (like me), don't add any more water. However, if you want a runnier sauce, blend in another 60 ml (2 fl oz/¼ cup) water.

Transfer the sauce to an airtight container and refrigerate until ready to use (the sauce will keep for up to 1 week).

While the sauce is cooling, prepare the filling. Heat 60 ml (2 fl oz/¼ cup) water in a large frying pan over a medium heat. Add the onion and sauté for 3–4 minutes, then throw in the garlic and jalapeño. Sauté for 2–3 minutes, or until the onion is translucent.

Add the tempeh and spices and cook until the tempeh just starts to brown and turn crispy. Toss in the kale and corn and cook for another 3 minutes until it starts to soften. Season with salt to taste. Remove from the heat and cover the pan with a lid until you're ready to eat.

Peel the skin off the sweet potato and mash, then season with paprika, salt and pepper.

Heat the corn tortillas in a dry frying pan for 1–2 minutes on each side until warm and soft (just before they go crispy).

Finally, it's time to get creative. I love to spread a layer of the mashed sweet potato on the taco, creating a soft base for the ingredients to be layered upon. Lightly top with the cabbage and sliced avocado before drizzling on the creamy cashew cheese sauce and salsa. Serve with some lime wedges on the side and the coriander, if using. Provecho!

JACKSON LONG AND AARON STUBER
THOUGHT FOR FOOD

Jackson and Aaron are a couple of elite endurance athletes who love nerding out on the nitty gritty details of the science behind good health and elite performance. They also like to take epic dumps! Sounds strange, but it's not a joke; there's a vast body of research showing that the quality of our bowel movements is a great indicator of our overall health. All the focus of the public nutrition and health conversation seems to be centered around the right ratios of carbohydrates, protein and fats, while basically ignoring what is arguably the most important nutrient of them all: fibre. Most of us don't eat enough fibre, and the truth is that if all we did was focus on eating a high-fibre diet, most of our health problems would go away.

Jackson and Aaron are compassionate and adventurous, they like to eat plants and push their bodies in the mountains of Colorado. They want to make a healthy, plant-based lifestyle practical for everyone with no dogma and drama, just science. 'Thought For Food' is the embodiment of their mission to help us all feel that little bit lighter on our feet after a regular 'epic dump'!

THE EVIDENCE—BASED ATHLETE POWER BOWL

A common saying about athletic performance is 'train hard, recover harder', and we believe it. Recovery is where the true gains are made, and food is a critical component of becoming a better athlete.

Many foods have been studied and shown to be potent performance enhancers, and this post-workout recovery bowl is packed with many of them, containing a variety of nutrient-dense plant foods rich in inflammation-fighting compounds to speed up your recovery.

The beetroot (beets) and rocket (arugula) are two of the highest sources of naturally occurring nitrates, which open up the blood vessels and drive more oxygen to our muscles. The sweet potato provides glycogen-replenishing carbohydrates and calories, while the pepitas (pumpkin seeds) are a fantastic source of iron. Topping it with nutritional yeast has been shown to boost immune-system function and decrease the incidence of upper respiratory infections in athletes, keeping them healthy and able to train more frequently. **Serves 1-2**

giant handful of rocket (arugula)
70 g (2½ oz/½ cup) grated beetroot (beets)
185 g (6½ oz/1 cup) green lentils, cooked or canned
½ avocado, sliced
1 Japanese (purple) sweet potato, baked or steamed then chopped (use any sweet potato if you can't find the purple ones)
1 tablespoon tahini
liquid aminos, to taste
handful of pepitas (pumpkin seeds)
sriracha, to taste
nutritional yeast, to taste

Place the rocket in the bottom of a large serving bowl. Add the beetroot, lentils, avocado and cooked sweet potato.

Top with the tahini, liquid aminos, pepitas, sriracha and some nutritional yeast, to taste.

Eat after a tough workout and enjoy the potent recovery powers of these nutrient-dense and evidence-based plant foods.

VICTORIA LISSACK

Victoria Lissack is a powerful woman in every sense of the word. After a successful, decade-long career as a litigation lawyer, she swapped the courtroom for the gym.

She's now a professional strength and body-composition coach, yoga teacher and athlete in her own right. As an ethical vegan first and foremost, she uses her training and competitive bodybuilding as a billboard for ethical veganism and a plant-based lifestyle.

She leads by example, showing people everywhere in no uncertain terms that there is power in compassion and that the ethical choice is also one that progresses you towards your best self.

SUPER EASY SWEET POTATO SMOOTHIE BOWL

Sweet potatoes are a key part of my diet, both on and off season. As well as being delicious, they are a rich source of fibre and contain an amazing array of vitamins and minerals, including iron, selenium, calcium, vitamin C and many of the B vitamins. They are also high in the antioxidant beta-carotene. Many of us have been baking, steaming and mashing them for years, but did you know that sweet potatoes also make a fantastic creamy base for a sweet smoothie bowl? This version is higher in carbohydrates and lower in fat, making it perfect as a post-workout meal (and if you add a scoop of your favourite plant-based protein powder, it packs a serious protein punch). It's also a great breakfast choice or afternoon snack when you want something sweet, cold and clean with a little more sustenance than a smoothie.
Serves 1

1 medium sweet potato
1 small, ripe banana, peeled and frozen
250 ml (8½ fl oz/1 cup) chilled, unsweetened almond milk or plant-based milk of your choice
125 ml (4 fl oz/½ cup) chilled coconut water
1 scoop vanilla or natural-flavoured, plant-based protein powder (optional)
toppings of your choice, such as shredded coconut, raspberries and blueberries, but superfoods and other fruits also work well

Preheat the oven to 220°C (430°F).

Place the sweet potato directly on the oven rack and bake for 45 minutes to 1 hour until very tender and the flesh can be easily pierced with a knife. Remove from the oven and leave to cool completely.

Scoop out the soft flesh of the potato and place it in a blender with the frozen banana. Blitz together until thick and smooth (do not over-blend, or you will lose the thickness).

Slowly add the almond milk and coconut water, blending on low speed as you go to mix well. Add the protein powder, if using, and blend gently to combine.

Pour the smoothie into a serving bowl. It should be served cold, so if it is a little warm, refrigerate for 15–20 minutes before serving. Add your chosen toppings and enjoy.

A DOG LOVES REPETITION
by Andrew

My dog Bruno the Doberman ate more or less exactly the same meal every single day for his entire life, and every single day he was jumping out of his skin with excitement when meal time came around. We don't have to be quite so monotonous with our eating, but it's definitely worth exploring the idea of minimalism in relation to our food choices. Find a few simple meals that you really enjoy and repeat them over and over. Having simple, easy, healthy meals locked and loaded at all times really reduces decision fatigue and frees up our brain space to get creative with other aspects of life. The bonus is that it makes healthy eating even easier, and it's friendly on your wallet, too!

MAT GRILLS

I had no idea who Mat was until I got a message from him one day, asking if I was free to help crew for him at an ultra-marathon. My first thought was that it was a strange request from someone I didn't know. My second thought was how much I admired all the ultra-distance athletes I'd read about over the years and how cool it would be to see an event like that first hand. I got the OK from the boss (Mandy) and headed off for the weekend to the 'Down Under 135', a 217km/135 mile race about an hour's drive from home.

It turned out to be a great decision and one of the most awe-inspiring weekends of my life. Mat was underprepared for the race, but he pushed on regardless, through immense suffering. I watched his calf muscles dance under his skin as though his legs were filled with small snakes, and I watched him brush it off like it was nothing and push on into the distance. I was privileged to share the trail and chat with him for 18 km when he was clearly suffering and at the end of his rope. You learn a lot about someone in that situation, and I learned that I'm happy to call him a friend.

Mat is a proud and passionate vegan with over 35 ultra-marathons to his name, including some of the country's toughest and most gnarly. His example leaves no room for doubt that epic things are possible with plants.

'THE FROTH IS HIGH' SALAD

I came up with this recipe because I love BIG salads and sweet potato is my favourite vegetable! I love the traditional kumara mixed with the creaminess of the Japanese sweet potato...delicious! Combined with the crunch of the cos lettuce and the epic dressing, this dish will be a winner for friends and family, or for you to enjoy on your own after a big day of adventuring! This salad ain't no ordinary green dish....it will get your froth high!! It'll stick to your ribs, fill you up and leave you satisfied....if you can finish it! Rip in! Feeds one hungry ultra-runner or four as a side salad.

2 medium Japanese (purple) sweet potatoes
1–2 medium sweet potatoes
1 baby cos (romaine) lettuce
1 x 120 g (4½ oz) bag baby spinach
1–2 corn cobs, kernels removed
10–15 mini Roma tomatoes, halved or
 quartered
sriracha, to serve
Dressing
1 heaped tablespoon tahini
½ teaspoon fresh chilli paste
1 tablespoon tamari
3 tablespoons apple-cider vinegar
juice of 1 lemon

Preheat the oven to 180°C (350°F).

Trim the ends off your sweet potatoes and cut into medium-sized chunks. Place on a baking tray lined with baking paper and bake for 1 hour. Flip the spuds halfway through cooking.

Trim your lettuce, wash, dry and tear roughly onto a serving plate or into a salad bowl.

Dump the bag of spinach on top and mix together.

Add the corn kernels, nibbling any residual corn off the cobs (fresh, raw corn is the bomb!)

Add the tomatoes to the baking tray with the spuds for the last 10–15 minutes of cooking time. Roast until caramelised.

To prepare the dressing, combine all the ingredients in a small bowl, mix well and set aside (refrigerate if you prefer a thicker dressing). If you prefer a runnier dressing, let it down with a little water.

Add the roasted spuds and potatoes to your salad, then drizzle with your desired amount of dressing (I like a lot), then finish with a little (or a lot, in my case) of sriracha.

Get into it and let the flavours dominate your tastebuds!

CHEFS

I've often said, 'make your food boring and your life interesting'. To me, this doesn't mean we should never enjoy our food or eat anything interesting, it's simply an acknowledgement that food should not be the be-all and end-all of our existence. For most of my life, I associated delicious food with junk (and misery), but these chefs have shown me that this couldn't be further from the truth.

The following chapter is a cornucopia of gastronomic splendour, with a foodgasm on every page. The most dedicated of foodies will be pleased to know that, thanks to the skill of these people, you can now have your (potato) cake and eat it too. Every one of these trail-blazing chefs takes great pride in creating amazing dishes that will make your taste buds dance, while also providing your body with supreme fuel and, best of all, no guilt!

CHEF AJ

I had long admired Chef AJ as someone who had fought and won a similar battle with food addiction: she bucked the typical vegan stereotype by being overweight, sick and addicted to junk foods.

She found her own solution to her addiction by embracing the science behind calorie density and eating unprocessed plant foods. Before I made the trip to LA for the Healthy Lifestyle Expo, we had never spoken or met; as far I knew she had no idea I existed. Then I got an email asking how I like to eat my potatoes and telling me not to worry about finding spuds on the other side of the globe – she had my back and would make sure I was well fed.

True to her word, she turned up at the first day of the conference with boxes and bags of spuds cooked in different ways, and she kept them coming for the next few days. She was busy with her own presentations and cooking demos, but on top of that, she made it her business to make sure I was looked after. A

couple of days later, she even invited me to her house for dinner where she introduced me to the Hawaiian purple sweet potato, and thus began a love affair (with the potato – though AJ is pretty great too!) that shows no signs of slowing down.

On my next trip, I was fortunate enough to take a judge's seat in the famous 'Iron Chef' cook-off between AJ and Chef Bravo (see page 125), which was an unforgettable experience. I've never eaten better food before or since than the exquisite, heavenly feast I had that day. I still can't believe that it was possible to make that kind of food with only unprocessed plant foods – much less that it was all guilt-free!

AJ is a true gem, a firecracker of unbridled energy and enthusiasm, who wants nothing more than to see people succeed in health and in life and to have a great time doing it.

THE MCDOUGALL/GOLDHAMER CAULIFLOWER RISOTTO SWEET POTATO STACK STACK

ΨΨΨΨΨΨ

For the past seven years, I have had the privilege of working as a guest chef and presenter at the annual TrueNorth Health Center's 'Holiday Extravaganza'. For the past three years, I competed in an SOS-free Iron Chef competition against their Executive Chef, Ramses Bravo. Every year, he wins the savoury round and I win the dessert round. Well, last year, it was a complete role reversal and it renewed my faith in my culinary skills when I actually beat him in the savoury round. The three secret ingredients were chosen by the three plant-based celebrity judges: Mary McDougall (who chose sweet potatoes), Dr Alan Goldhamer (who chose cauliflower), and Cathy Fisher (who chose red capsicum/bell pepper), hence the name of this outstanding dish. Serves 6-8

4 large white or orange sweet potatoes, roasted, cooled, skins removed and flesh sliced

Risotto filling
1 shallot, finely minced
340 g (12 oz) riced cauliflower (see Note)
220 g (8 oz) zucchini (courgette), finely diced
340 g (12 oz) finely diced hearts of palm or water chestnuts, soaked in water to remove the salt (optional) (or another 220 g/8 oz zucchini/courgette if not using hearts of palm or water chestnuts)
250 ml (8½ fl oz/1 cup) Red capsicum (bell pepper) sauce (see below)
1 teaspoon salt-free seasoning of your choice, or more to taste

Red capsicum (bell pepper) sauce
1 large capsicum (bell pepper), cored and seeds removed, roughly chopped
3 cloves garlic
110 g (3 oz) sundried tomatoes, oil and salt-free

120 g (4½ oz) riced cauliflower
125 ml (4 fl oz/½ cup) unsweetened plant-based milk of your choice
1 teaspoon smoked paprika
½ teaspoon chipotle powder

To make the red capsicum sauce, combine all the ingredients in a blender and blitz until smooth. Set aside.

Heat a frying pan over a medium heat and sauté the shallot in 60 ml (2 fl oz/¼ cup) water until translucent.

Add the cauliflower and sauté until soft, adding extra water if the pan becomes too dry. Add the zucchini and the hearts of palm, if using, and cook for another couple of minutes.

Stir in the red capsicum sauce and seasoning until well combined, then allow to heat through for another 2–3 minutes.

To serve, place a thick slice of the sweet potato on a serving plate. Top with a scoop of the risotto filling, then place another thick slice of potato on top, followed by another scoop of the risotto filling, and so on.

Note

Riced cauliflower is now available in the refrigerator or freezer section of many supermarkets. If you cannot find it, simply rice the cauliflower yourself using a food processor fitted with the shredding blade.

SWEET POTATO MOUSSE ͟ᵂ CARAMELISED APPLES

At the most recent Healthy Taste of Sacramento, I competed in an Iron Chef. The secret ingredients were sweet potato and apples, and I won the dessert round. Mary McDougall, Andrew 'Spud Fit' Taylor, and Linda Middlesworth were the judges, who apparently all have excellent taste. Serves 4-6

Sweet potato mousse
400 g (14 oz/2 cups) roasted sweet potatoes
250 g (9 oz/1 cup) ripe roasted pears (tinned or jarred is fine)
½ teaspoon ground cinnamon or apple-pie spice
Caramelised apples
235 g (8 oz/2 cups) apple finely diced (see Note)
250 ml (8½ fl oz/1 cup) unsweetened pear juice, or water
½ teaspoon ground cinnamon or apple-pie spice

Preheat the oven to 200°C (400°F).

To make the mousse, combine all the ingredients in a food processor and blitz until smooth. Set aside.

For the caramelised apples, combine all the ingredients in a small sauté pan and bring to the boil over a high heat. Cook until the apples are soft and all the liquid is gone.

To serve, place a few spoonfuls of mousse on a serving plate and top with the caramelised apples.

Note

The sweeter the variety of apple that you use, the sweeter the topping will be.

CAULIFLOWER BISQUE

🍴🍴🍴🍴🍴🍴

This is a variation of the Broccoli Bisque adapted from and inspired by Mary McDougall. One day I was making it at TrueNorth Health Center and all they had was unsweetened vanilla almond milk and, believe it or not, it was delicious. Serves 4

1 large cauliflower, core and stem included
900 g (2 lb) white sweet potatoes (Hannah yams)
1.5 litres (51 fl oz/6 cups) vegetable stock or water
1 large onion
8 garlic cloves
2 tablespoons dried dill
2 tablespoons salt-free seasoning of your choice
1 tablespoon smoked paprika
1 litre (34 fl oz/4 cups) plant-based milk of your choice
4 tablespoons salt-free stone ground mustard or Dijon mustard
4 tablespoons nutritional yeast (optional)

Option 1

Combine all the ingredients, except for the plant milk, mustard and nutritional yeast, in a pressure cooker and cook on high pressure for 10 minutes. Release the pressure and add the milk, mustard and nutritional yeast (if using).

Option 2

Combine all the ingredients, except for the plant milk, mustard and nutritional yeast, in a slow cooker and cook for 6-8 hours. Then add the milk, mustard and nutritional yeast (if using).

Option 3

Combine all the ingredients, except for the plant milk, mustard and nutritional yeast, and boil until everything is very soft. Then add the milk, mustard and nutritional yeast (if using).

Purée with a hand-held blender, or carefully transfer it to a blender and blitz until smooth.

Note

This bisque is delicious served over black, red or wild rice. I like to garnish it with pico de gallo, a Mexican salsa made with tomatoes, diced onions, green chillies, garlic and coriander.

CHEF DEL SROUFE

Del's interest in cooking began when he was just 8 years old. By the time he was 13, he was cooking meals for his family, much to his mum's delight! After a brief flirtation with the world of business, Del decided that selling suits was not for him and he returned to his culinary roots. He has since worked in a variety of restaurants, run his own bakery and personal-chef services, and run his own cooking classes.

He really found his groove when he joined 'Wellness Forum Foods' as executive chef, delivering great tasting plant-based meals all over the US. The author of several best-selling cookbooks, including 'Forks Over Knives' and 'The China Study', Chef Del Sroufe had spent over 30 weeks at the top of the New York Times best-seller list. His book 'Better Than Vegan' documents how he lost over 90 kg (200 lb) following a low-fat, plant-based diet.

DEL'S BIG BREAKFAST CASSEROLE

ψψψψψψ

This recipe is not your everyday breakfast food. Make it for company or when you're in the mood to spend a little extra time in the kitchen on a Saturday morning. Serves 6-8

4 medium red-skinned potatoes, scrubbed, thinly sliced and steamed
3 large onions, thinly sliced, and 2 medium onions, diced
450 g (1 lb) firm tofu
1 x 340 g (12 oz) packet extra-firm silken tofu
1 red capsicum (bell pepper), diced
220 g (8 oz) sliced button mushrooms
280 g (10 oz) frozen broccoli florets, thawed
4 garlic cloves, minced
1 tablespoon dried basil
1 teaspoon dried sage
½ teaspoon ground fennel seeds
1 teaspoon chilli flakes
6 tablespoons nutritional yeast
sea salt, to taste
½ teaspoon black pepper

Preheat the oven to 180°C (350°F).

Heat a large frying pan over a medium heat and sauté the sliced onion in 60 ml (2 fl oz/¼ cup) water until caramelised, about 12 minutes. Set aside.

Combine the firm and silken tofu in a large bowl and mash to the consistency of ricotta cheese. Set aside.

Heat another large frying pan over a medium–high heat. Add the diced onion, capsicum, mushrooms and broccoli, and sauté for 5–6 minutes until the vegetables are tender. Add the garlic and spices and cook for another minute. Mix into the tofu mixture, along with the nutritional yeast, salt and pepper.

Press the tofu filling into a 22 x 33 cm (9 × 13 in) non-stick baking dish. Top with the steamed potatoes and the caramelised onions. Bake for 45 minutes.

EATING THE RAINBOW
by Andrew

When most of us think of potatoes, we just think of the standard white potatoes that are most common in the shops. We might've also seen a red-skinned potato from time to time, and that's about it. You might be surprised to know that there are well over 1,000 varieties of potatoes, mostly originating in the Andes of South America. Many of these are too bitter to eat, but serve an important purpose in maintaining biodiversity of plant life in their native areas. Around 200 varieties are commonly eaten around the world, coming in all sorts of weird and wonderful shapes, sizes and colours, including deep purples and blues, reds and pinks, yellows, oranges and whites. The more colourful potatoes tend to also be higher in powerful health-promoting antioxidants. You truly can eat the rainbow with potatoes. Well, almost... just avoid them if they're green; they've probably been in the cupboard too long!

CHEF NA

Chef Na was creating jars of Thai sauces and pastes in Thailand, so that people from all over the world could experience authentic Thai flavours. She gained attention when she was featured in a prominent business newspaper and was then invited to Australia to help restaurants capture her signature flavours. She has worked with some of Melbourne's top restaurants and cafés, ensuring that health-conscious eaters have plenty of plant-based Thai options to whet their appetites. She now runs 'Chef Na's Plant-Based Kitchen' with her husband Frankie, making the most delicious, authentic and healthy restaurant-quality meals, all available to us at home. Chef Na is fully committed to sustainability, good health and cruelty-free living, and takes great pride in giving others not just the ingredients but also the confidence to take their cooking to the next level.

TOM YUM SOUP
<u>w</u> POTATO

What I love most about tom yum is the fine balance of the five main flavours in Thai cuisine: sweet, sour, bitter, salty and spicy. The secret behind making this tangy dish authentic is the addition of coriander (cilantro) root. The beckoning fragrance never fails to transport me back to Thailand, no matter how briefly. **Serves 2**

1 lemongrass stalk
1 tablespoon galangal, peeled and grated
1 tablespoon chopped coriander (cilantro) root
2 garlic cloves, minced
1 onion, diced
1.25 litres (42 fl oz/5 cups) vegetable stock or water
500 g (1 lb 2 oz) potatoes
5 cherry tomatoes, halved
45 g (1½ oz/½ cup) sliced mushrooms
4 tablespoons soy sauce
pinch of coconut sugar
2 Thai red chillies, diced (or 2 tablespoons Sriracha), plus extra to garnish (optional)
3 kaffir lime leaves, central stems removed
1 teaspoon lime juice, plus extra if desired
handful of chopped coriander (cilantro) and lime wedges, to garnish

Slice the thick ends off the lemongrass stalk, then use the handle of your knife to pound stalk lightly. This helps to release the oils. Slice the stalk into 2–3 pieces.

Heat a large stockpot over a medium–high heat. Once hot, add the lemongrass, galangal, coriander root, garlic and onion. Cook, in a little stock, for 1–2 minutes, stirring regularly until fragrant.

Add the remaining vegetable stock and potatoes, and bring to the boil. Once boiling, reduce the heat to medium–low and cover with a lid. Simmer for 10–15 minutes, or until the potato is cooked.

Remove the lemongrass from the pot and discard.

Add cherry tomatoes and mushrooms and continue simmering, uncovered, for approximately 5 minutes, or until the vegetables are soft.

Season the soup with soy sauce and coconut sugar, and stir to mix well.

Taste the soup and adjust the seasoning by adding the chillies or Sriracha, if desired.

Add the kaffir lime leaves and lime juice at the end to give a citrusy taste. Garnish with the coriander and lime wedges.

CHEF RAMSES BRAVO

Chef Bravo originally trained as a regular chef, with no interest in plant-based eating and most definitely no interest in working as a vegan chef! After a few years gaining weight while working in hotels, the perfect storm of circumstance arose that allowed Alan Goldhamer of True North Health Centre to talk/coerce him into taking a job as head chef. Chef Bravo was originally horrified that, on top of cooking vegan food, he would also not be using any oil, sugar or salt, and nothing processed! In his eyes, this was not what it meant to be a chef, but he thought, nevermind, he needed a job and he could just stick around for six months and then move on to a place that appreciated real food. Fast forward more than eight years, and Chef Bravo remains in this job as an award-winning vegan chef, healthier

and lighter than ever, and with several whole food, plant-based cookbooks to his name. He loves his job and his food and even travels the country teaching people how to cook delicious whole plant food.

I met Chef Bravo when Dr Klaper took me on a tour of True North Health Centre. I was already impressed with the lunch I had there, and it was nice to meet the man who cooked it. I was totally unprepared for the incredible food he and AJ would make for me when I judged the Iron Chef contest the following weekend. Chef Bravo proves beyond doubt that you can eat the most incredible, delicious food without using anything that's not provided by nature in the form of whole plant foods.

BAKED YAMS
CORN CHOW CHOW

I love this recipe because it's a play on a very old concept that still works to this day: sweet and sour. This combination will continue to be a winner as long as food is prepared by anyone. Serves 4

4 medium sweet potatoes, cut in half lengthways
310 g (11 oz/2 cups) sliced red onion
½ teaspoon dried oregano
½ teaspoon mustard seeds, toasted
¼ teaspoon ground turmeric, toasted
800 g (1 lb 12 oz/4 cups) fresh or frozen corn kernels
60 ml (2 fl oz/¼ cup) apple-cider vinegar
1 teaspoon chopped fresh thyme

Preheat the oven to 190°C (375°F).

Place the yams on a baking tray lined with baking paper and bake for 35–40 minutes, or until golden brown.

Heat a large saucepan over a medium heat for 1–2 minutes. Dry sauté the red onions for 2 minutes, stirring often. Add the oregano, mustard seeds and turmeric and cook for another minute.

Stir in the corn and cook for 2 minutes. Add the vinegar and cover the pan. Reduce the heat to low and cook for 5 minutes.

When the baked yams are cooked, transfer them to a serving plate. Stir the thyme into the corn chow chow, then pour over the yams.

EMILY HAZELL
SEROTONIN EATERY

Emily hosted an evening with Dr Klaper at her café in Melbourne and provided me with some of the best potatoes I had eaten that year, despite them not being available on her menu. The name for Emily's café, Serotonin Eatery, Exercise and Education, came from the idea that we should eat and behave in a way that maximises serotonin production in our bodies. Serotonin is our major feel-good hormone, and as someone who has struggled with mental health, I love the idea that we can exert so much influence on our own mood simply by changing what we put on our plate. Emily battled her own mental demons and eventually found her way through with the help of a significant change in diet. Whole-plant foods create the perfect environment for serotonin production in our gut, so much so that, to Emily, good food felt like the ultimate happiness drug! Serotonin is the only café or restaurant that I know that puts a huge emphasis on education as well. It's one thing to give people good food, it's another entirely to help them understand the whats, whys and hows of it all. Emily resolved to become a dealer and through her café and her team of 'Serotonin Dealers', is now dedicated to sharing the happiness with every meal.

SEROTONIN SPUD

At Serotonin Eatery we promote mood-boosting foods for a natural happiness high – that's why we love this recipe!
Each orange spud contains high levels of the antioxidant vitamins, A and C, which work together to boost the immune system. They also contain potassium and are very high in soluble fibre. Fibre slows down the absorption of sugar into your bloodstream, which regulates your blood sugar levels and keeps them balanced. This helps you maintain a good mood! Need more science? Okay here goes!
Potatoes produce an insulin response in your body. Insulin allows tryptophan to get into your brain and this turns into the neurotransmitter Serotonin, a contributor to your well being. At Serotonin Eatery, we feed you Happiness :) Serves 6

3 large sweet potatoes
1 large avocado, mashed
sliced lime wedge, to serve
Tomatillo dressing
680 g (1½ lb/12 medium) tomatillos, rinsed and husks removed
1 to 2 medium jalapeños, stemmed (see note)
½ medium white onion, chopped
7 g (¼ cup/¼ oz) coriander (cilantro)
2 tablespoons lime juice (add up to 60 ml/2 oz/¼ cup more if you love lime juice)
½ – 1 teaspoon sea salt, to taste
Slaw
¼ head green cabbage, thinly sliced
¼ head red cabbage, thinly sliced
1 bunch of coriander (cilantro), roughly chopped
1 cup spring onions (scallions), chopped
125 g (½ cup/4 oz) fresh or frozen corn kernels
1 x 420 g (15 oz) tin red kidney beans
Cashew sour cream
155 g (1 cup/5½ oz) cup raw cashews (see note)
90 ml (¼ cup plus 2 tablespoons/3 fl oz) fresh

lemon juice
125 ml (½ cup/4 fl oz) water
1 teaspoon nutritional yeast
¼ teaspoon salt

Note

Omit jalapeños for mild salsa, use 1 jalapeño for medium salsa and 2 jalapeños for hot salsa. Spiciness will depend on heat of actual peppers used.

If you don't have a high powered blender, soak the cashews for a few hours or overnight.

Preheat the oven to 180°C (350°F).

Pierce the sweet potato a few times, then place on a baking tray lined with aluminium foil. Bake for 45 minutes to 1 hour, until tender.

Make the tomatillo dressing by combining all the ingredients in a blender and blitzing until smooth. Set aside.

To make the slaw, combine all the ingredients in a large mixing bowl, add the tomatillo dressing and toss until well combined.

For the cashew sour cream, combine all the ingredients in a blender and blitz until smooth. Refrigerate for at least an hour for a thicker consistency.

To serve, cut the sweet potato in half and top with slaw, a drizzle of cashew sour cream, the mashed avocado and a lime wedge.

EMMA MOIGNARD
SOULFUL VEGAN FOOD

Emma's enthusiasm and energy is contagious; she throws everything she has at her work and is rewarded with many smiling faces and happy tummies. At 17 years old, Emma was recognised as one of the best apprentice chefs in Victoria, and was fully qualified by the age of just 19. She started Soulful Vegan Food in an effort to show people how delicious and healthy food can be, without the need for any animal products. Originally cooking from home to sell to locals, she received great support from her community and her business has now morphed into a thriving little café with food that nourishes the body and the soul.

As a long-time ethical vegan, Emma is working hard to reach as many hearts and minds as possible. She sees that the best way to get there is through the stomach! I often go to visit her café, but rarely get a chance to chat with Emma, I guess that's a good sign!

LOADED SWEET POTATO
MACARONI CHEESE

I love this recipe because macaroni and cheese was a staple growing up with my old best friend. Together with sweet beetroot (beet) purée, mushie mince and creamy avocado, you can't go wrong! Serves 2

2 sweet potatoes
155 g (5½ oz/1 cup) macaroni
250 ml (8½ fl oz/1 cup) soy milk, or plant-based milk of your choice
1 tablespoon nutritional yeast
1 teaspoon onion powder
1 teaspoon garlic powder
6 large mushrooms, roughly chopped
1 x 400 g (14 oz) tin diced tomatoes
1 teaspoon dried mixed herbs
1 teaspoon paprika
1 tablespoon maple syrup
1 x 450 g (1 lb) tin baby beetroot (beets), drained
1 avocado
1 tablespoon vegan mayonnaise, for drizzling (optional - see page 7)
pinch of sea salt and freshly ground black pepper

Pierce the sweet potato a few times then place on a baking tray lined with baking paper. Bake for 45 minutes to 1 hour until tender and the flesh is easily pierced with a sharp knife.

Bring a saucepan of water to the boil over a high heat. Add the macaroni and cook according to the packet instructions. Drain, then return to the pan.

Mix in the soy milk, nutritional yeast, onion and garlic powders and some salt and pepper to taste.

Combine the mushrooms, tomatoes, herbs, paprika and maple syrup in a saucepan and blitz with a hand-held blender until roughly mixed. Set over a medium heat and bring to a light simmer.

Place the beetroot in a blender and blitz to a purée. Smash the avocado and set aside.

To assemble, slice the potato in half lengthways and scoop some of its flesh to the side to make room for the filling. Top with the macaroni mixture, beetroot purée and smashed avocado. Drizzle over some vegan mayonnaise, if using, to finish it off.

EMMA ROCHE

It's a common refrain that 'eating healthy is just too expensive'. Emma Roche put that one to bed quick smart with her first book titled 'Whole Food Plant Based on $5 A Day'. As a struggling student, Emma refused to compromise on her health. Creativity is often unleashed through the tightest of confines. Necessity is the mother of invention, and necessity dictated that Emma would find a way to make the healthiest food affordable.

Emma is intent on showing people that not only is plant-based eating both healthy and delicious, but it can also satisfy the hip pocket of even the thriftiest of uni students. With help from Emma, the proverbial 'starving artist' will soon be a thing of the past!

CRISPY BAKED POTATO HASH W HOMEMADE SALSA

🍴🍴🍴🍴🍴🍴

I love this recipe because it's so simple and versatile. Enjoy it as a savoury breakfast, or serve it with salad or vegetables as a mian meal. You can play around with the herbs and spices in this recipe if you like, to create new and delicious flavour combinations. Serves 2

Hash
1 kg (2 lbs) washed potatoes, small diced
1 small onion, finely diced
1 clove garlic, minced
1 teaspoon paprika
½ teaspoon smoked paprika or chipotle powder (optional)
1 teaspoon dried oregano
¼ teaspoon black pepper

Salsa
1 x 400 g (14 oz) tin salt-free diced tomatoes
2 tablespoons salt-free tomato paste
¼ teaspoon onion powder
¼ teaspoon garlic granules
⅛ teaspoon smoked paprika or chipotle powder
¼ teaspoon ground cumin
¼ teaspoon ground coriander seed
¼ teaspoon dried oregano
1½ tablespoons white vinegar
2 tablespoons finely chopped jalapenos (more if you want it spicier!)
1 tablespoon pure maple syrup
fresh ground black pepper, to taste

Preheat oven to 210°C (400°F).

Line one large (or two small) baking trays with baking paper.

Place the diced potatoes in a large mixing bowl, and add the onion, garlic, paprika, smoked paprika (or chipotle powder), oregano, and black pepper. Mix well so that the onions, garlic and spices are evenly distributed. Spread the potatoes in an even layer on the baking tray.

Bake for 15 minutes, then remove the tray from the oven and toss the potatoes with a spatula to redistribute. Return tray to the oven and bake for a further 10-15 minutes until the potatoes are golden brown and crisp.

While the potatoes cook, prepare the salsa. Combine all salsa ingredients in a large mixing bowl. Stir until well combined. If you'd like your salsa less chunky, transfer it to a blender or food processor, and pulse at intervals until you reach the desired consistency. Transfer salsa to a bowl or container, and refrigerate until serving time.

Remove potatoes from the oven and serve immediately, topped with plenty of salsa.

POTATO & BROCOLLI DAL

Dal is a traditional Indian stew made using dried, split pulses. It's a staple in my household because it's an affordable, filling, one-pot meal. There's also something so comforting about sitting down with a nice big bowl of this – especially when it's packed full of potatoes!

Serves 4-6

1 medium onion, diced
3 cloves garlic, minced
1 tablespoon grated fresh ginger
2 medium carrots, diced
⅔ cup water
2 tablespoons mild curry powder
2 teaspoons ground cumin
½ teaspoon chilli powder
1 kg (2 lbs) potatoes, washed and cut into small chunks
2 cups red lentils
5 cups low-sodium vegetable stock
500 g (1 lb) broccoli, cut into small florets
¼ teaspoon salt (optional)
black pepper, to taste

Combine the onion, garlic, ginger and carrot in a stockpot with 170 ml (5½ fl oz/⅔ cup) water. Sauté for 5–6 minutes until the onions and carrots are soft.

Add the spices and cook, stirring continuously, for 2 minutes until the spices become fragrant. Add a little more water if necessary to prevent the spices from sticking.

Add the potatoes, lentils and vegetable stock and bring to the boil over a high heat. Reduce the heat to medium, cover and simmer for 20 minutes.

Remove the lid. Add the broccoli and stir through. Cover again and simmer for a further 10 minutes.

Remove pot from the heat and let the dal stand for 5 minutes. Season to taste with salt, if using, and freshly ground pepper.

TYPES OF POTATOES

by Mandy

We know that there are literally thousands of varieties of potatoes, but broadly speaking, for cooking purposes, potatoes are usually classed into two categories: 'waxy' or 'floury/starchy'.

WAXY 'BOILING' POTATOES

Waxy potatoes are high in moisture and low in starch. These potatoes don't disintegrate when they're cooked, making them great for dishes where holding their form is important such as scalloped potatoes, salads, soups, casseroles etc.

Varieties of waxy potatoes: Nadine, Dutch Cream, Nicola, Cara, Charlotte, New Potatoes

FLOURY/STARCHY 'BAKING' POTATOES

These potatoes have a high starch content. They break apart when they're cooked, making them great for fluffy baked, roasted or mashed potatoes and chips (fries), but less suitable for salads.

Varieties of floury potatoes:

King Edward, Russets, Maris Piper, Coliban, Idaho, sweet potatoes

All-purpose potatoes are just that - all-purpose. They may tend towards being either waxy or floury, but you can use them in most applications and they'll get the job done. Examples are Yukon Gold, Desiree, Sebago, Kennebec.

A WORD ON THE NAMING OF POTATOES, SWEET POTATOES AND YAMS:

Though also a root vegetable, the sweet potato is not actually a potato at all - in fact botanically speaking it is only distantly related! While potatoes are a nightshade, from the same family as tomatoes and aubergines (eggplant), sweet potatoes are from the same family as morning glory. The reason for the naming mix up comes from the early European explorers combining the words 'papa' (Quechua - potato) and 'batata' (Taino - sweet potato) to make 'potato'.

Native to the tropical areas of the Americas, it is also biologically completely unrelated to the yam - though the terms themselves are often used interchangeably. True yams, related to lilies and grasses, are native to Africa and Asia, have a much coarser skin and are much higher in starch. They are also far less sweet - chances are when you think you've been eating a yam, you've actually been eating a sweet potato!

IIDA
A KITCHEN FAIRYTALE

When Iida was diagnosed with inflammatory arthritis she was shocked; arthritis is supposed to be just for old people! The pain and swelling in her knees and other joints didn't lie though. She was suffering, and her doctors told her there was no cure. She dutifully took the medication despite it feeling like poison, but had to stop when it gave her an allergic reaction. The only option left was to sort it out on her own. After some research, she ditched dairy, started drinking green smoothies and doing yoga and things greatly improved. Then, with help from Clint Paddison (see page 79), she took her health to the next level by ditching all animal products and processed foods entirely. These days, she is healthier than ever, living life totally free of the symptoms of rheumatoid arthritis. Iida wants people to know that they don't have to continue suffering from this terrible disease – it can be a thing of the past with a few simple dietary changes, and she is here to show you how to make it delicious and fun!

FINNISH SUMMER SOUP

♈ ♈ ♈ ♈ ♈ ♈

This dish takes me back to grandma and grandpa's summer house in Finland, where, as children, we would get to pick fresh chives to sprinkle on top of our soup. It is my plant-based version of a traditional Finnish soup, which is light and divine in the summer, but also wonderfully warming in the winter. It is best made with unpeeled but scrubbed, fresh summer vegetables, which will release the maximum amount of flavour if cooked from cold water that is then brought to the boil. The dill stems create some lovely flavour when added to the cooking water, whereas the dill tops are best added uncooked just before serving. The almond milk and flour can be left out for a clear version of the soup.

In Finland, various types of rye bread (for example crispbread or sourdough bread) are classic accompaniments to soups. My favourite bread topping is mashed avocado with lemon, a sprinkling of salt, black pepper and chilli flakes. **Serves 6**

1 onion, finely chopped
5 large potatoes, cut into large chunks
4 large carrots, thickly sliced
1 cauliflower head, separated into florets
11/2 teaspoons Himalayan pink salt
1 tablespoon gluten-free plain (all-purpose) flour
375 ml (121/2 fl oz/11/2 cups) almond milk, or plant-based milk of your choice
130 g (41/2 oz/1 cup) frozen peas
1 teaspoon chopped fresh dill, stems and tops separated
1 teaspoon chopped fresh chives

Combine all the vegetables, except the peas, in a large stockpot with 1.5 litres (51 fl oz/6 cups) cold water. Add the salt and bring to the boil over a high heat.

Reduce the heat to medium and simmer for 15 minutes.

In a small bowl, mix together the flour and enough of the milk to form a paste. Stir well to break up any lumps.

Add the peas to the soup, pour in the remaining milk, then stir in the flour mixture.

Boil for a couple of minutes, stirring occasionally, then turn off the heat and sprinkle the dill and chives over the top just before serving.

CHEF KATIE MAE
THE CULINARY GYM

I was privileged enough to witness one of Katie's cooking classes first-hand where she blew my mind with sweet potato noodles – I didn't even know that was possible! She also took me along to my first ever (and still only) whole food, plant-based party. It's a rare experience to go to a party, eat as much as you want and then leave feeling great.

Weight loss and good health happens first and foremost in the kitchen. We all know this, yet most of us focus our efforts in the gym instead. Katie Mae is changing all that by helping us to build our kitchen fitness through 'The Culinary Gym'. As the core cooking instructor in two of the country's most successful health centres – True North and The McDougall Program (see page 19) – Katie has seen countless patients recover from debilitating chronic diseases and change their lives forever. She knows that for many of us, the key to maintaining good health is building kitchen skills and learning to cook with fresh, wholesome ingredients. For Katie, being kitchen-fit is the first step on the path to physical, emotional and mental health. When you are kitchen-fit, you feel at ease preparing great food that you look forward to eating.

SPICY SWEET POTATO HASH

I think sweet potatoes are a perfect breakfast food, especially with flavour like this. The pinch of spice and squeeze of sweet orange make every bite amazing. Plus, it's quick and easy to make – ready in 20 minutes with little hands-on prep. Enjoy this plant-based hash for breakfast, lunch or dinner. **Serves 2**

1 small onion, diced
1 sweet potato, cut into 1 cm (½ in) dice
60–125 ml (2–4 fl oz/¼–½ cup) orange juice (about 2 oranges, juiced)
1 tablespoon almond butter
½ teaspoon ground cinnamon
½ teaspoon chilli powder
pinch of chilli flakes, or more to taste
½ bunch of kale, shredded

Heat a large frying pan over a high heat, add the onion and potato, cover the pan and sauté in a little water for 3 minutes, stirring occasionally.

In a small bowl, whisk the orange juice and almond butter together. Pour this dressing into the frying pan and stir. Reduce the heat to medium–low and cook for 5 minutes.

Mix in the spices and kale and simmer for another 3 minutes. The dish is ready when the potatoes are fully cooked and the kale has a bright green colour.

SELECTING AND STORING POTATOES
by Mandy

Look for firm, smooth potatoes, without cuts or major discolouration. In particular, be on the lookout for any green areas – this is an indication that there is a buildup of solanine, a bitter-tasting chemical that is produced when the potato is exposed to too much light. Small amounts of green can usually be cut away by peeling, but if you eat too much it can potentially make you slightly nauseous or even really ill with a range of nasty symptoms you definitely want to avoid. Also avoid potatoes with 'eyes' – they are trying to sprout!

To avoid these problems, potatoes should be stored in a cool, dark, dry, well-ventilated place - not the fridge, it's too cold, and not under the sink - too hot!

TALITHA CASE
THE PLANTRITIONIST

Talitha's culinary curiosity was heavily influenced by her father, whose pantry was always stocked with all sorts of weird and wonderful ingredients. During her upbringing, creativity and experimentation were highly valued and encouraged, and the search for intense and inspiring flavours from all over the world was neverending.

When Talitha first became plant-based, she thought she was waving goodbye to her family's foodie tradition in exchange for bland and boring plant foods. At first, she searched high and low for great websites and cookbooks that would fulfill her hunger for serious flavour, but something was always missing. The only option left was for her to go back to her experimental, creative roots and start using whole plant foods to recreate the big, bold, flavoursome dishes she grew up with.

'The Plantritionist' was born out of this, and she now shares her skills, tips and recipes for the home cooks of the world who like healthy plants with big flavour.

CURRIED GREEN LENTILS W BEETROOT MASH

Potatoes and lentils, for me, go together like Australia and summer – they're made for each other. The lentils are incredibly flavoursome and complement the creaminess of the potatoes and the sweetness of the beetroot (beets). A generous squeeze of lemon or lime, a few extra chilli flakes for the chilli lovers, and a slice of avocado and small dollop of vegan yoghurt, and you have yourself a dish that is delicious, impressive and will have you wishing you had gone vegan sooner. Serves 4

Mash
1 kg (2 lb 3 oz) white potatoes, peeled
200 g (7 oz) tinned beetroot (beets), drained
2 tablespoons plant-based milk
½ small red onion, diced
sea salt and freshly ground black pepper

Lentils
1 onion, diced
2 garlic cloves, crushed
370 g (13 oz/2 cups) dried green lentils
2 teaspoons ground cumin
2 teaspoons ground ginger
2 teaspoons ground coriander
1 teaspoon ground turmeric
½ teaspoon curry powder
½ teaspoon ground cardomom
½ teaspoon ground cinnamon
½ teaspoon cayenne pepper
1 bird's-eye chilli, diced
1 large handful baby spinach leaves
sea salt and freshly ground black pepper, to taste

To serve
coconut yoghurt
sliced avocado
fresh coriander (cilantro), torn
fresh lemon or lime wedges

Add all the ingredients (except for the spinach leaves) for the lentils to a large stockpot. Add 1.5 litres (51 fl oz/6 cups) water, cover with a lid and set over a medium heat. Once the mixture begins to bubble, reduce the heat to low, remove the lid and simmer gently for about 40 minutes to allow the liquid to reduce. Stir occasionally to avoid the lentils sticking to the bottom of the pot. If you need to, add a little more water.

While the lentils are cooking, put the potatoes in a large stockpot and cover with cold water. Bring to the boil over a high heat and cook until the potatoes are tender and almost falling apart. Drain, return the potatoes to the pot and add the beetroot and milk. Mash together well, then season with salt and pepper to taste.

Once the lentils are cooked, remove from the heat and stir in the spinach. Leave the lentils to rest for 10 minutes, then check and adjust the seasoning, adding more salt and pepper if desired.

Serve topped with coconut yoghurt, avocado, coriander and some citrus wedges on the side.

TONI OKAMOTO & MICHELLE CEHN

Toni Okamoto is the founder of 'Plant-Based on a Budget', the popular website, food blog, and meal plan that shows you how to save dough by eating veggies. She's also the author of 'The Super Easy Vegan Slow Cooker Cookbook'. 'Plant-Based on a Budget' has been featured in 'Reader's Digest', 'US News' and 'World Report', and more. Toni's also a regular presence on the FOX affiliate in Sacramento, where she teaches viewers how to break their meat habit without breaking their budget, and was featured in the popular documentary, 'What the Health'. Toni is a burrito enthusiast who lives in Sacramento, CA, and spends her free time swing dancing across the county.

Michelle Cehn is on a mission to empower her fellow earthlings to make kind choices and enjoy the many benefits of a plant-powered life. She is the founder of the popular vegan lifestyle website 'World of Vegan', co-author of the 'Plant-Based on a Budget Meal Plan' and 'The Friendly Vegan Cookbook', and co-creator of 'The Dairy Detox'. An avid photographer and filmmaker, Michelle has produced hundreds of videos for her own YouTube channel as well as for leading vegan organizations. She has dedicated her life to helping people align their actions with their values, and provides inspiration and support to help make lifestyle changes easy and fun.

SWEET POTATO TOAST

Sweet potatoes are one of the healthiest foods on the planet. They're packed with Vitamin A, potassium and fibre, and they're a wonderful food to incorporate into your diet whenever possible.

So, how about swapping out that boring white bread you toast up in the morning with some colourful sweet potato toast? It's healthy, it's delicious, it's even photogenic (for all you Instagram-lovers!). **Serves 1**

½ **large sweet potato**
oil- and sugar-free peanut butter, to taste
sugar-free jam (jelly), to taste
½ **banana, sliced**

Preheat the oven to 200°C (400°F).

Slice the sweet potato in half lengthways, then thinly slice using a sharp knife (see Note).

Arrange the slices on a baking tray lined with baking paper and bake for 20 minutes, or until soft.

Top with peanut butter, jam and sliced banana. Enjoy!

Note

If the pieces are too thick, they will take significantly longer to cook.

THE ORIGINAL POTATO CHIPS!
by Andrew

Some of the world's greatest dishes include the humble potato. Potatoes were first cultivated in Peru up to 10,000 years ago, and have since found their way into cultures all over the world. Just about every country and culture has a traditional, potato-based dish. One of the earliest examples is Chuño, which has been a traditional Peruvian dish for at least 8,000 years. It involves slicing and freeze-drying potatoes, which allows them to be stored for years. Chuño helped many Andean tribes survive in times of drought, and became a staple food for Incan armies. In the 16th century Chuño even helped to build the Spanish Empire, as it was fed to silver miners who helped to generate vast wealth for the government.

ADAM GUTHRIE
THE I FEEL GOOD PROGRAM

The whole room was silent as Adam told us about how he, a seemingly fit and healthy surfer, suffered a heart attack in the ocean one morning. His doctor told him that he needed to be on daily medication for the rest of his life. Adam wasn't ready or willing to accept this life sentence, so he decided to do everything in his power to find a better way. He started by learning how to treat himself with kindness, love and respect, which led to a whole new life.

The morning after his talk, we hugged and cried together as he told me the story of how he lost 30 kg (66 lb), got off all his medications and even ended up completing one of the world's toughest endurance events – an Ironman triathlon. We've been

mates ever since and he's always been there for Mandy and I with a calming word or an insightful observation whenever we've needed it.

After all this, Adam realised that he could use his knowledge and experience to become a role model and educator, inspiring others to find life after a heart attack – and many other health issues for that matter – simply by telling his story. He now combines his training as a professional chef and e-Cornell certified nutritionist with his passion for plant- based nutrition and self-care, to help others overcome chronic illnesses and move along the path to boundless energy through his 'I Feel Good Program'.

RAINBOW JUNGLE CURRY

🍴🍴🍴🍴🍴🍴

I love this recipe because it's so quick and easy to prepare, and only requires one pot or a wok. It's super fresh and vibrant. The colours are amazing and just looking at it makes me feel happy. Serves 2

100 g (3½ oz) brown-rice vermicelli noodles
1 large potato, cut into small dice
90 g (3 oz/1½ cups) chopped broccoli florets
235 g (8½ oz/1½ cups) grated carrots
2 baby bok choy (pak choy), thinly sliced lengthways
115 g (4 oz/1½ cups) shredded purple cabbage
handful of green beans, topped and tailed, sliced on diagonal
handful of fresh Thai basil
1 tablespoon sesame seeds, for topping
juice of 1 lime
Broth
1 small onion, diced
1 tablespoon minced fresh ginger
2 tablespoons vegan red curry paste
1 tablespoon hot chilli paste (sambal oelek) (optional)
1 litre (34 fl oz/4 cups) vegetable stock
2 tablespoons date or coconut sugar
2 tablespoons vegan fish sauce (optional)
2 tablespoons soy sauce

Soak the noodles in a bowl of boiling water for 15 minutes. When soft, drain and rinse.

Meanwhile, to make the broth, heat a wok over a high heat. Add the onion and ginger and stir-fry for 3–5 minutes. Add the curry and chilli pastes and stir-fry for 1 minute.

Add the stock, sugar, fish sauce and soy sauce, then add the potato. Simmer for 10 minutes.

Add all the remaining vegetables and half the basil to the wok, stir. Simmer for 2–3 minutes, then add the lime juice.

Place half the noodles into a serving bowl and ladle over the broth and vegetables. Top with the remaining fresh basil leaves and sprinkle over some sesame seeds.

AMANDA RAE

Amanda is another A-grade chef who provided me with food when I was away from home (I was certainly spoiled on my trip to LA!) I'd never heard of her before and was blown away by her kindness when she contacted me out of the blue with her offer to provide me with some potato meals to get me through.

After swinging on the pendulum between junk-food vegan and super-healthy plant eater, Amanda decided it was time to hone her skills at New York's 'Natural Gourmet Institute'. After culinary school, Amanda developed 'Groundleaf.co' as a platform to share what she was creating for her friends and family. It has since become her life's passion, where she shares clean, fresh and simple meals using herbs and spices to create flavorful dishes that bring out the best in plant foods. Her mission is to offer savoury, hearty, whole food recipes to get you started – and keep you going – on your plant-based journey.

POTATO & MUSHROOM STEW

We were inspired to create this stew after making a batch of one of our all-time favourite recipes: mushroom stroganoff. We wanted to create something that was hearty and filling, while still being entirely plant-based, and we did it! The combination of mushrooms, potatoes, corn and spinach, in addition to fresh herbs and spices, gives this stew a great flavour. This recipe is also really versatile – try subbing in soaked cannellini beans for a tasty alternative. We like to serve this stew over greens or your favourite whole grain for a complete meal that comes together quickly

Serves 2

450 g (1 lb) white or cremini mushrooms, quartered
1 onion, diced
3 garlic cloves, minced
500–750 ml (17–25½ fl oz/2–3 cups) mushroom stock (see Note)
1 tablespoon tomato paste (concentrated purée)
1 tablespoon chickpea or oat flour
95 g (3¼ oz/½ cup) dried black lentils
1 tablespoon Dijon mustard
1 tablespoon tamari
1 tablespoon chopped fresh thyme
1/2 tablespoon chopped fresh rosemary
1 teaspoon sea salt
1/4 teaspoon freshly ground black pepper
1 large russet potato, diced
150 g (5½ oz/1 cup) frozen corn kernels
50 g (1¾ oz/1 cup) fresh baby spinach

Heat a large frying pan over a medium heat. Add the mushrooms and onion and sauté in a little water until cooked through and starting to brown. Add the garlic and sauté for a couple more minutes.

Remove about one-quarter of the mushroom mixture and blend it with 60 ml (2 fl oz/¼ cup) mushroom stock until smooth.

Add the tomato paste to the pan with the mushroom mixture and stir. Add the flour and mix well.

Add the remaining mushroom stock, lentils, Dijon, tamari, herbs, salt and pepper. Bring to a gentle boil, then reduce the heat and simmer for 10 minutes.

Add the potato and simmer for another 15 minutes. Once the potato has softened, add the blended mushroom mixture, the corn and the spinach. Stir until well combined and heated through.

Serve as it is, or on top of your favourite greens or grains.

Note

You can use store-bought mushroom stock or make your own.

AMRITA
CRAZY VEGAN KITCHEN

Amrita doesn't mince words! She's hilarious, blunt, creative, sometimes confronting and always the best kind of crazy.

She's proud and passionate about animals and food (in that order), and she wants nothing more than to help you develop those passions too, through her popular blog, 'Crazy Vegan Kitchen'.

Her motto is 'anything you can make, I can make vegan' and, having trained at 'Le Cordon Bleu London', she's got the skills to back it up. Amrita loves her tatts almost as much as her cats, and this dark sorceress of vegan recipes is sure to win over even the most hardcore carnivore.

OIL—FREE HERB & MUSTARD POTATO SALAD

Y Y Y Y Y Y Y

I love this recipe because, unlike most potato salads, it uses both sweet potato and regular potato to change things up a little. The herb and mustard dressing is tangy, healthy, delicious and deceivingly creamy.

Serves 3-4

3 red-skinned potatoes, cut into large cubes
1 small sweet potato, cut into large cubes
Herb & mustard dressing
4 tablespoons wholegrain mustard
1 tablespoon Dijon mustard
1½ tablespoons maple syrup
2 tablespoons lemon juice
1 teaspoon minced garlic
1 teaspoon onion powder
4 tablespoons warm water
15 g (½ oz/½ cup) finely chopped parsley
15 g (½ oz/¼ cup) chopped chives
sea salt and freshly ground black pepper, to taste

Fill a large saucepan with cold water and add the potatoes. Bring to the boil over a high heat and boil until the potatoes are tender and can be easily pierced with a sharp knife, about 15 minutes.

Meanwhile, prepare dressing by combining the mustards, maple syrup, lemon juice, garlic and onion powder with 80 ml (2½ fl oz/⅓ cup) warm water in a large mixing bowl. Whisk to combine, then add the chopped herbs and season to taste.

Once the potatoes are tender, drain and add them to the bowl of dressing.

Gently toss to coat the potatoes, then check and adjust the seasoning if necessary.

Serve warm or at room temperature.

ANJA CASS

One of my first ever speeches was to quite a big crowd at World Vegan Day during my year of eating spuds. After I got off stage, Anja Cass asked me for a photo together and I remember having trouble putting two words together as I was thinking 'what the hell do you want a pic with me for? I should be the one asking you!'

Anja was shocked when she was diagnosed with a heart aneurysm; she was too young and healthy for that. Not content to simply follow doctors' orders, she got to researching on her own and after reading 'The China Study' she set about making some serious changes to her diet.

She went plant-based overnight and, in the following four months, she lost 24 kg (52 lb) and her cholesterol dropped like a stone. All signs were good except that she had trouble finding decent recipes. She started experimenting and, after a lot of positive feedback from friends and family, decided to start her wildly successful YouTube channel, 'Cooking With Plants'.

MEDITERRANEAN STYLE POTATO SALAD

This is a fresh and tasty potato salad with lots of delicious Mediterranean flavours. It is great as a side dish, or as a meal in itself. I like to serve this with falafels and hummus for a Middle Eastern twist. It is also a great salad to take on picnics because it stays fresh and can be assembled just before you are about to eat. Serves 4-6

5 potatoes, boiled in their skins, then peeled
1 small Lebanese (short) cucumber, diced
1 small red onion, sliced lengthways
1 x 400 g (14 oz) tin chickpeas, drained and rinsed
½ handful of fresh mint leaves, thinly sliced
1–2 teaspoons sumac
1–2 teaspoons ground cumin
¼ teaspoon freshly ground black pepper
½ teaspoon fine sea salt
juice of ½ small lemon

Slice the cooked potatoes, then spread them out on a large serving platter.

Scatter the cucumber and red onion over the top of the potatoes, then top with the chickpeas.

Sprinkle with fresh mint leaves and the spices, then drizzle with the lemon juice.

Note

If the salad needs more moisture, toss through a little of the chickpea brine to give the dish an oil-style feel without the extra fat.

CARYN DUGAN

Caryn Dugan is the irrepressible and unstoppable superwoman behind 'ST. Louis Veg Girl'. She always considered herself to be a health-conscious eater, diligently counting the calories and macronutrients that went into her ready-made TV dinners. Caryn ignored the laundry list of unpronounceable ingredients and numbers on her 'food' because to her, healthy meant skinny and she had that side of things well under control. This all changed when she lost her dad to cancer and then was diagnosed herself shortly after. The mercifully short battle with cancer that followed ignited a flame within her that still burns brightly to this day.

The 'Rouxbe Cooking School'-trained chef considers herself an educator first and foremost. Caryn's ability to create mouthwatering flavours is matched by her knowledge of the health benefits behind her creations, having learned from the best at Neal Barnard's (see page 21) 'Food For Life' program. She has made it her mission to share her knowledge of the powerful immune-boosting capabilities of plant foods and will stop at nothing to get 'a plant on every plate'.

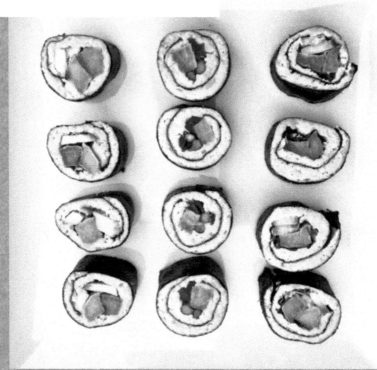

SUSHI

⛙⛙⛙⛙⛙⛙

A new take on vegetarian sushi, this roll swaps out the vast amount of white rice you would usually easily eat (do you just pop sushi in your mouth like me?) and subs in tempeh, which is a fabulously minimally processed, nutrient-dense fermented baby soybean cake. Using sweet potatoes and other vegetables to fill them makes these rolls even healthier. They're easy to fill and roll up, and you can quickly fill a platter to feed a party.
Makes 2 large or 3 medium rolls

1 sweet potato
220 g (8 oz) tempeh
1 tablespoon tahini
1 tablespoon yellow miso paste
1 tablespoon rice-wine vinegar
¾ tablespoon date paste or other liquid sweetener
½ tablespoon tamari
1½ teaspoons onion powder
2–3 nori sheets
vegetables of your choice, for filling (avocado, asparagus, zucchini/courgette, grated carrot, pickled onions, etc.)
wasabi, pickled ginger and black sesame seeds, to garnish (optional)

Preheat the oven to 220°C (430°F).

Peel the potato and cut into fries. Place on a baking tray lined with baking paper and bake for 20 minutes, then remove and leave to cool.

Break up the tempeh into large pieces and steam for 10 minutes in a steamer basket suspended over a saucepan of simmering water.

Transfer the tempeh to a food processor, along with the tahini, miso paste, vinegar, date paste, tamari and onion powder. Pulse to combine, just enough to ensure there are no large chunks of tempeh.

Transfer the mixture to a bowl and set aside. Fill a small bowl with cold water.

On a clean work surface, lay down a bamboo sushi roller and place a sheet of nori on top. Spread a scoop of tempeh out with your fingers. When your fingers begin to stick to it, dip them in the cold water. Leave about one-quarter of the nori sheet uncovered at the top.

Place two rows of your chosen vegetables horizontally on top of the tempeh, at the edge

nearest to you.

Using the bamboo mat, gently lift and roll the mat up, over and around, creating a roll. Squeeze the roll gently to seal, then unroll the mat and use a little of the cold water to seal the uncovered edge of the nori sheet to create a firm roll.

Place the roll seam side down and slice with a very sharp knife. Repeat until all the sheets, tempeh and vegetables have been used. Sprinkle the sushi with sesame seeds and serve with wasabi and pickled ginger.

CATHY FISHER

When looking through Cathy's website a couple of years back, I found my favourite recipe of all time, titled 'The Big Pile of Food'. In that moment, I knew I'd found a chef I could get behind. 'Straight Up Food' is the name of her website and book, and it is exactly as it sounds: real food, real simple, real good. Cathy recognises the inherent beauty in simplicity and her phenomenal skills mean that she can turn the most straightforward of dishes into finger-licking crowd pleasers.

For over eight years, Cathy has been a culinary instructor at TrueNorth Health Centre and the McDougall Program (see page 19), where people take comfort in her no-fuss approach to nutrition and cooking. Cathy wants to take the mystery out of cooking and eating health-promoting food, but also wants to get you excited about the endless possibilities that are available if you're ready to explore.

BEEFLESS STEW

TTTTTT

This beefless stew is one my most popular recipes. I love it and it appeals to others because it looks just like the beef stew many of us grew up eating. This health-promoting version does not, however, sacrifice flavour for health. Portobello mushrooms stand in beautifully for the beef, and even meat-eaters don't seem to mind, because the dish is so tasty. I also love it because it's colourful and much easier to make than traditional beef stew. **Serves 6-8**

1½ large onions, sliced into 1.75 cm (¾ in) pieces
3 medium carrots, sliced lengthways into 1.75 cm (¾ in) pieces
3 celery stalks, cut into 1.75 cm (¾ in) pieces
2 Portobello mushrooms, cut into 1.75 cm (¾ in) pieces
1½ tablespoons finely chopped garlic
900 g (2 lb) white potatoes, peeled and cut into .5 cm (¾ in) chunks
90 g (3 oz/1/3 cup) tomato paste (concentrated purée)
1 tablespoon dried Italian herbs
1 tablespoon paprika
2 teaspoons finely chopped rosemary
235 g (8½ oz/1½ cups) cooked peas
10 g (¼ oz/½ cup) chopped parsley

Heat 1 tablespoon of water in a stockpot over a medium–high heat. When the water starts to sputter, add the onion, carrot and celery, and cook, stirring frequently, for about 8 minutes, adding more water as needed to stop the vegetables sticking.

Stir in the mushrooms and garlic and continue cooking, stirring constantly, for another 5 minutes, adding water as needed.

Add the 1.25 litres (42 fl oz/5 cups) water, the potatoes, tomato paste, Italian herbs and the paprika, and bring to the boil over a high heat. Reduce the heat to medium–low and stir in the rosemary. Cover and cook for 25–30 minutes, stirring occasionally, or until the carrots and potatoes are very tender.

Add the peas and cook for another 5 minutes. Transfer 2 cups of the stew to a blender and blend briefly, then stir the mixture back into the pot to thicken the stew. Stir in the parsley.

HOW TO GROW YOUR OWN POTATOES

by Andrew

One of the reasons potatoes took over the world is that they are so easy to grow. You can even grow potatoes in a hessian sack in your kitchen. Put a couple of inches of soil in the bottom of a sack, then put your potatoes on top. Add enough soil to just cover the potatoes, water them and wait for them to grow! As the green shoots start to appear, gradually add more soil until the bag is full and you have a flowering green plant on top! Allow the plant to die, then tip the bag upside-down and harvest your spuds.

ACTIVISTS

When we choose a car, we want to know how fuel efficient it is. When we buy a washing machine, we want to know how much electricity and water it uses. We reduce, reuse and recycle where we can because we are aware that our actions have an impact on the environment. Food is the world's number one consumer product by quite a margin, so no discussion of diet is complete without considering the impact of our choices. We can't thrive as a species without an environment that is conducive to our health and happiness. We can't celebrate our achievements as a race if they come at the expense of our fellow earthlings.

Everyone in this book is an activist at heart, but the people in this chapter focus their efforts towards promoting peace, kindness and respect to animals and our environment.

PETER SINGER

Peter Singer is a moral philosopher and revolutionary thinker who has challenged conventional thought on a wide range of issues for more than five decades.

His 1975 book 'Animal Liberation' was the first philosophy book I ever read. It totally changed the way I thought and felt about the idea of 'animal rights', and it introduced me to the ideas of discrimination through 'speciesism' and 'the greatest good' as a measure of ethical choices. 'Animal Liberation' is widely regarded in the animal liberation movement as a founding document of sorts, with its central idea being that our treatment of animals should be considered in terms of their ability to experience suffering above all other considerations.

I've since maintained a great interest in philosophy in general and have continued to follow Peter's work (I even took a sick day – don't tell the boss! – to attend one of his lectures). I've never even done that for a rock star or a sports event.

In my opinion, veganism and vegans are too often wrongly passed off as being overly emotional, spiritual and 'airy fairy' in our ideas of how the world should be. I really love the way Peter removes emotion from the decision-making process and uses pure logic and reasoning to arrive at the conclusion that the consumption of animals and their use in other forms is unjust and unethical.

SICHUAN STIR FRIED POTATOES
W VINEGAR

This is one of my favorite Sichuan dishes. The potatoes are thinly sliced, like matchsticks, and soaked in salt water. Then they are drained and stir fried, with Sichuan peppercorns, dry red chillies, sugar and vinegar. That gives the dish its unique flavor, salty and spicy with a touch of sweetness. Sichuan peppercorns are available at many Chinese groceries. If you can't get them, you can use ordinary pepper, but it won't be the same. The texture of the potatoes is another unusual feature – they should be firm, even a little crunchy. Serves 2

6 medium or 3 large potatoes, cut into matchsticks
1 teaspoon salt
3 teaspoons - ½ cup vegetable stock, for frying (see Note)
4 large dried red chillies, chopped (see Note)
3 teaspoons Sichuan peppercorns, crushed
2 teaspoons sugar
5 teaspoons black vinegar (use Chinkiang vinegar, if possible)
more salt, to taste

Peel the potatoes and cut them into matchsticks.

Put them in bowl of cold water into which you have put the teaspoon of salt. Leave them for at least 10 minutes, then drain.

Put the vegetable stock, chillies, and Sichuan peppercorns into a wok over medium heat. When the peppercorns start to sizzle, add the potatoes.

Fry for about 4 minutes. Then add the sugar and vinegar. Continue to stir fry, tasting to see if they are crunchy but not completely raw. Add salt to taste, and serve hot.

Note

When I make this dish for myself, I use a little cooking oil to stir fry the potatoes. Because this is a 'no oil' cookbook, however, I have replaced the oil with a little vegetable stock. For this version, I also suggest using a non-stick wok.

Use chillies to taste - you might start with fewer, and work your way up if you can handle it.

ANIMALS AUSTRALIA

In my view, no organisation has had a bigger impact on animal rights in my home country than Animals Australia.

Their tireless work has resulted in huge mainstream coverage for many important issues in the last decade. Their investigations have exposed the nation and the world to the horrible conditions and treatment of animals on factory farms and slaughterhouses, in live export ships and puppy mills, as well as in horse and greyhound racing. They've ignited debates in parliament and challenged (and changed) laws in the highest court in the land.

They educate through outreach at universities and public events, as well as through huge advertising campaigns on TV and radio. While many animal-rights organisations seem to attract derision and scorn from the general public, somehow Animals Australia manages to get their message out in an inclusive way that seeks to unite us all around a common belief: that animals deserve to be treated with care and compassion.

They believe that we can create a kinder world for all by fostering respect for animals, and that our treatment of animals reflects who we are as individuals and as a society.

Animals Australia
for a *kinder* world

HEARTY CORN & POTATO CHOWDER

🍴🍴🍴🍴🍴🍴

Rich and creamy, this warming soup is delicious as is – or you can give it a surprise chilli kick with a zesty lime and coriander garnish. If chilli isn't your thing, try serving this classic soup with some fresh parsley and garlic croutons instead.
Serves 4-6

3 garlic cloves, minced
1 brown onion, diced
2 celery stalks, diced
3 medium potatoes, peeled and diced
1 litre (34 fl oz/4 cups) vegan stock
1 tablespoon white miso paste
3-4 fresh corn cobs, kernels removed, (reserve ½ cup of kernels to garnish)
375 ml (12½ fl oz/1½ cups) soy milk or plant-based milk of your choice
sea salt and freshly ground black pepper, to taste
To serve
coriander (cilantro)
chilli flakes (optional)

EATING THE PLANET
by Andrew

Animal agriculture produces more greenhouse gasses than the entire transport sector combined, making it the highest-polluting industry on earth. It is also responsible for more land use, deforestation (mostly for feed crops - grass-fed meat uses even more land) and water than any other industry, while also creating more ocean dead zones through faeces and fertiliser runoff than any other industry. If you don't eat any animal products, you could run a Hummer non-stop while leaving all the lights on and your shower running 24 hours a day, 365 days a year and you'd still use less water, fossil fuels and land, and produce less greenhouse gas, than the average meat eater. If we care about the environment then reducing or, better still, eliminating animal products from our diet is a no-brainer.

Heat a large sauce pan over a medium heat and sauté the garlic, onion and celery in 1–3 tablespoons of water for 4–5 minutes. Add the potato, stock and miso paste and stir to combine.

Cook for about 15 minutes, stirring frequently, until the potatoes are soft. Stir in the corn kernels and milk, and cook for a further 5 minutes.

Remove half of the soup to a blender and blitz to a creamy consistency. Pour the blended soup back into the pan, stir through, and season to taste with salt and pepper. Don't have a blender?

No problem! You can use a hand-held blender, or even a potato masher to combine everything together.

Ladle the soup into serving bowls and garnish with the reserved corn kernels, sliced chilli and coriander leaves. Sprinkle with a pinch of dried chilli flakes, if desired, and a squeeze of lime juice.

ANIMAL LIBERATION VICTORIA

Organisations like Animal Liberation Victoria (ALV), who expose the truth of what goes on in factory farms and slaughterhouses, are dear to my heart. Watching video footage of industry-standard 'processing methods' was a big part of my own decision to go vegan, and without the brave souls who risk their own safety and freedom to obtain such footage it might never have happened.

ALV was founded in 1978 with the mission of saving lives and ending animal exploitation. Embracing the principle of non-violence, ALV rescue teams openly investigate animal factories to rescue sick and injured animals and to document the unethical conditions hidden from public view. They also educate the public about cruelty-free living and promote veganism as the ethical, rational and earth-friendly lifestyle that it is.

SWEET POTATO & KALE CHILLI

ᵭᵭᵭᵭᵭᵭ

We love this recipe because it is packed with protein, complex carbohydrates and vegies, providing a filling, tasty and nutritionally balanced meal that you can eat throughout the week. Serves 2

310 ml (10½ fl oz/1¼ cups) vegetable stock
1 onion, diced
2 garlic cloves, minced
1½ teaspoons smoked paprika
1 teaspoon ground cumin
1 teaspoon ground coriander
½ teaspoon cayenne pepper
½ teaspoon ground cinnamon
½ teaspoon coconut sugar
1 x 400 g (14 oz) tin chopped tomatoes
1 large sweet potato, peeled and diced
1 x 400 g (14 oz) tin black beans, drained and rinsed
5 stalks kale, chopped
25 g (1 oz/½ cup) chopped coriander (cilantro) leaves
sea salt and freshly ground black pepper, to taste
cooked brown rice, to serve
1 teaspoon plain soy yoghurt, to serve (optional)

Heat 60 ml (2 fl oz/¼ cup) of the vegetable stock in a large frying pan over a medium heat and cook the onion and garlic until translucent and fragrant.

Add the spices and coconut sugar, stir, and cook for 1 minute, then add the tomatoes, and remaining vegetables stock and mix well.

Add the sweet potato and cover the pan with a lid. Simmer gently for 30–35 minutes, or until the sweet potato is tender. Stir in the black beans and cook for a further 10 minutes, then add the kale and simmer until just wilted, about 5 minutes.

Season with salt and pepper to taste, then remove from the heat and stir in the coriander. Serve with brown rice and yoghurt, if using.

ANJI BEE
HAPPY HEALTHY VEGAN

Anji Bee is half of one of my favourite YouTube channels, 'Happy Healthy Vegan', along with her partner Ryan Lum. When I was invited to appear on 'The Doctors' TV show, the first thing I did was hit Google to find out what the show was. I found an episode where the hosts did their best to make Anji and Ryan look like fools for eating a vegan diet, including lots of bananas. This episode was the reason I decided that I wouldn't go on the show unless Dr McDougall (see page 19) could come on with me for support. Since then, I've been a fan of theirs and was excited to be able to hang out and jam with them at a party in LA. What you see is what you get with Anji; she's laid back, relaxed, fun and welcoming - not to mention multi-talented!

Anji Bee is the lyricist/vocalist of indie band, 'Lovespirals', as well as a podcaster, vidcaster and author. She released her debut vegan cookbook, 'Keep It Carbed, Baby!', in 2016, highlighting her most popular Instagram posts featuring oil-free, salt-free, onion-and garlic-free, primarily gluten-free, whole food, plant-based recipes that comprise the bulk of what the duo eats on a regular basis.

'Happy Healthy Vegan' is Anji and Ryan's mission to help people embrace veganism by removing the mystery and helping people to understand how simple and easy it is. With a catalogue of over 1000 videos, they share their laid-back vegan lifestyle and show that it doesn't take a lot of planning or preparation to be successful. They bust myths and tackle mainstream misconceptions, calling out those who peddle misinformation along the way. Anji Bee leaves no doubt that the key to being a happy healthy vegan is to keep it carbed, baby!

GREEN BEAN & POTATO SUBJI

One of our local Krishna Temple restaurants serves what they call 'Subji'. I learned that this name translates to 'vegetable dish', and can mean just about any variety of plant-based Indian dish. This dry curry-style dish tastes extra yummy with a bit of asafoetida (also known as hing powder), which is traditionally used as a substitute for garlic and onions by various religious groups who avoid the use of allium plants.

Unfortunately, it must be heated in oil, so if you want to experiment with hing, you'll need to heat a dollop of coconut oil in your skillet before adding the potatoes and water to preheat the hing powder. I get around this by using an imported Indian curry powder that contains asafoetida as one ingredient.

Serves 4

450 g (1 lb) chopped potatoes (see Note)
450 g (1 lb) chopped green beans
450 g (1 lb) tinned chopped tomatoes
1 tablespoon Indian-style curry powder (or more, to taste)
freshly ground black pepper, to taste
370 g (13 oz/2 cups) cooked brown basmati rice, to serve (optional)
pinch of chilli flakes (optional)

Heat a frying pan over a medium–low heat. Add 60 ml (2 fl oz/¼ cup) water and the potatoes and cover with a lid.

Add the green beans, curry powder and optional chilli flakes, then mix well. If it starts to dry out as you continue cooking, add a little more water.

Once the potatoes and green beans are nearly soft – in about 20 minutes – add the tomatoes and mix well. Cook for another 5–10 minutes, until the potatoes are heated through but not breaking down. Season with black pepper to taste, and serve over optional basmati rice.

Note

Classic russet potatoes work well for this dish, but you can experiment with other steam-friendly varieties, like Yukon Golds. Also note that the more tomatoes you add, the saucier this dish turns out. You can add a tablespoon or two of tomato paste (concentrated purée) if you prefer a richer, thicker sauce.

ASH NAYATE

In a world full of passionate people with loud voices, Dr Ash Nayate is the calm within the storm. Sharing advice, insights and inspiration, her book teaches us about 'Staying Positive in a F*cked Up World'. She's a constant voice of logic and reason and a skilled communicator with a gift for opening people up to new perspectives and ideas. As an ethical vegan and a clinical neuropsychologist, Dr Nayate is acutely aware of the benefits of a vegan lifestyle in promoting brain health and mental wellbeing. This includes the physiological impact of a whole food, plant-based diet, as well as the profound psychological benefits of advocating for animal liberation. Her work in the vegan and activist communities includes supporting those who are struggling to cope with the social and psychological challenges of being vegan in a non-vegan world

ALL–DAY BREAKFAST POTATOES

This recipe is inspired by my love of all things breakfast, and is filling enough for either lunch or dinner. It's a versatile and toddler-approved recipe that works with almost any vegetable, and spices can be adjusted to suit all taste buds. Leftovers keep well in the fridge for the next day, and can be easily assembled for a quick meal. Serves 4

4 large white potatoes or 8 medium potatoes
freshly ground black pepper, to taste
Tofu scramble
1 onion, diced
2 garlic cloves, minced
1 block firm tofu, crumbled
½ teaspoon paprika (or more to taste)
1 teaspoon celery salt or salt-free vegetable stock powder
¼ teaspoon ground turmeric
1 teaspoon chilli flakes, plus extra to serve (optional)
310 g (11 oz/2 cups) assorted chopped vegetables like mushrooms, peas, capsicum (bell pepper), asparagus etc. (here, I have used corn, broccolini, and kale)
2 tablespoons nutritional yeast
Salsa
2 large tomatoes, chopped
7 g (¼ oz/¼ cup) chopped flat-leaf (Italian) parsley
7 g (¼ oz/¼ cup) chopped coriander (cilantro)
½ tablespoon lemon juice (or more to taste)

Preheat the oven to 180°C (350°F).

Place the potatoes onto baking tray lined with baking paper and pierce each with a fork.

Bake for 35–45 minutes, or until tender and the flesh is easily pierced with a knife.

To make the tofu scramble, heat 2 tablespoons water in a large frying pan over medium heat. Add the onion and garlic and sauté until softened.

Add the crumbled tofu, paprika, celery salt or stock powder, turmeric and chilli flakes (if using), and stir well to combine. (The tofu will release water as it cooks, so keep stirring for 2–3 minutes.)

Add the mixed vegetables and nutritional yeast and stir until well combined. Remove from the heat and cover with a lid to allow the vegetables to steam.

For the salsa, combine all the ingredients in a bowl and stir gently to combine.

To assemble, cut the baked potatoes into quarters or eighths. Serve the scrambled tofu and salsa on top. Add additional chilli flakes or black pepper, if desired.

CLARE MANN

Generating societal change is a massive job, and for it to be done right the people leading the charge have to be at their best. That's where Clare Mann comes in. After working with many vegan clients in her private psychology practice, Clare found that vegans experience a unique anguish unlike those involved in other social justice movements. She coined the term 'vystopia' to describe this vegan dystopia, in which vegans not only have to cope with the enormity of knowledge about large-scale animal cruelty, but also the trance-like collusion of non-vegans in propping up this unjust society.

Clare has authored several best-selling books on various aspects of being an effective activist. She's also an ethical leadership coach and Editor in Chief of the digital business magazine 'Ethical Futures: Conversations that Matter', which champions initiatives that are profitable and successful without abusing people, the environment or animals. As a long-time animal-rights campaigner, Clare has personally experienced the full gamut of emotional reactions to vystopia, and is dedicated to helping ease the burden felt by many in this movement.

ROAST POTATO SCRAMBLE W GHERKINS + ROASTED RED CAPSICUM

This is the perfect, easy-to-make comfort food with a kick. The gherkins make the dish unique, and the yeast flakes give a creamy consistency. Substantial yet not heavy, it's a dish I can quickly prepare even when returning home late at night. More recently, I've been able to use capsicums (bell peppers) and fresh herbs from my garden, making this an even healthier option, and turmeric is a powerful spice, known for its anti-inflammatory properties. A fantastic stand-by recipe that can be modified using roasted artichokes or olives instead of capsicums and gherkins.
Serves 2

1 small shallot, finely chopped
250 g (9 oz) firm tofu
2 tablespoons chopped roasted red capsicums (bell peppers)
1 medium tomato, sliced
1 level tablespoon chopped pickled gherkins
3 large tablespoons nutritional yeast
4 medium oven-roasted potatoes
1 teaspoon ground turmeric
1 teaspoon mixed dried herbs (or fresh herbs, if you prefer)
sea salt and freshly ground black pepper, to taste
pumpernickel or rye toast, to serve (optional)

Heat a frying pan over medium heat and fry the shallot in a little water until brown.

Crumble in the tofu, then add the capsicum, sliced tomato and gherkins. Mix together well. Add yeast flakes and stir until well combined.

Quarter the potatoes (leaving the skins on) and add to the mixture, then add the turmeric, herbs and a little water. Season to taste with salt and pepper and serve hot.

Serve on pumpernickel triangles or rye toast for a more substantial meal.

VICTORIA MORAN
MAIN STREET VEGAN

Victoria has been a driving force behind the plant-based movement for over three decades. Her iconic book, 'Main Street Vegan', was my first introduction to her work and I've been hooked ever since. She's another person who appeals to the teacher in me with her commitment to education and making healthy, vegan food and living accessible to the mainstream.

Victoria is multi-talented; she has written several best-selling books, hosts the award-winning 'Main Street Vegan Podcast', and produced the film, 'A Prayer for Compassion', to introduce vegan living to people of faith. She has trained many of the next generation of lifestyle coaches, educators and entrepreneurs through her 'Main Street Vegan Academy', and was even featured on 'Oprah' a couple of times.

Named as PETA's sexiest vegan over 50 in 2016, Victoria is still as prolific as ever, continuing to educate the masses and put healthy, vegan eating where it belongs: on the main street!

YOGI'S YELLOW POTATO CURRY

Comfort food meets Ayurvedic healing! I've been making some variations on this basic entrée for over twenty years. Back then, I thought the coriander, cumin, turmeric, cinnamon, cloves and black pepper were only there for flavour. That would have been reason enough, but I know now that these spices are health-promoters par excellence, with disease-fighting antioxidants galore. A favourite winter dish at our house, this curry offers not just the warmth and heartiness of the potatoes and beans, but also a lovely warming from the inside out that comes from the spices. And it's a virtually foolproof recipe. There's enough to stress over in life; there's no need to stress about dinner. Serves 4

Heat 3 tablespoons of the stock in a large frying pan over a medium heat. Add the garlic and sauté for 3 minutes.

Add the potatoes, green beans and carrots, then mix well. Top up with the remaining stock, then add all the spices and bring to the boil. Reduce the heat to low and cook, covered, for 15 minutes.

Add the chickpeas and simmer until the liquid has reduced by half.

Serve over rice (red rice and black rice are an interesting change from brown) with a side of mango chutney.

500 ml (17 fl oz/2 cups) vegetable stock
3 garlic cloves, minced
450 g (1 lb oz/2 cups) peeled and cubed waxy potatoes
250 g (9 oz/2 cups) fresh or frozen sliced green beans
2 carrots, thinly sliced
1 teaspoon ground coriander
1 teaspoon ground cumin
1 teaspoon ground turmeric
¼ teaspoon ground cinnamon
¼ teaspoon ground cloves
pinch of cayenne pepper
1¼ teaspoons sea salt
1 x 400 g (14 oz) tin chickpeas, drained
cooked rice, to serve
mango chutney, to serve

EFFECTIVE ACTIVISM

AMY KIDD, ANIMALS AUSTRALIA

Amy is a professional animal advocate, working with Animals Australia to create meaningful change for animals in the food system.

As animal lovers, it can be hard to know the best way to create change for them. Here are my top five tips for being a strong voice for animals and advocating for a vegan diet.

USE YOUR STRENGTHS

Just like animals, we're all different. Some of us love getting out and doing public outreach with a group and having positive and potentially life-changing conversations about animals. Some of us love reaching out to decision-makers or showing support to local businesses making choices that help animals. Some of us contribute our professional skills to the cause. Others help by supporting our favourite animal-protection organisations, and some of us love inspiring others by cooking up delicious, animal-friendly food to share with friends, family and colleagues. Find your strengths and use them to help create a kinder world. At the end of the day, simply being kind, open and empathetic is a powerful way to inspire others and help change the world for animals.

FIND LIKE-MINDED PEOPLE

Seeking out others who are as passionate about animals as you are can be a great way to get a sense of the strength of our community and what we can achieve together. Volunteering for an animal-protection organisation can be a great way to meet other animal advocates. If you're at university, find out if your campus has an animal society. You can also find local vegan and vegetarian groups on meetup.com, or join online groups on Facebook.

ADVOCATE WITH COMPASSION

Treat others with kindness, and you'll get kindness back.

• Share good food: Sharing delicious vegan food is one of the most powerful and positive ways you can help change perceptions about plant-based food and open your friends and family up to the idea of eating a different way.

• Cater to your audience: Finding common ground is a great starting point for productive conversations. If you're talking to a health-conscious friend, you might like to speak to them about the many health reasons to reduce meat, egg and dairy consumption. If your buddy is all about the environment, talk to them about the huge difference a meat-free diet can have on the planet.

• Celebrate every win: If your friend decides to do a vegan challenge, let them know how awesome they are and share your favourite recipes with them. If a family member decides to try eating dairy-free, help them out with some recommendations of your favourite dairy-free products. Knowing that they have your support can be exactly what they need when they're ready to take the next step for animals.

BE KIND TO YOURSELF

Animals need you and, for that reason, taking care of yourself is infinitely important.

• Avoid overexposing yourself to graphic cruelty: If you're already aware of the injustices animals face, and you're fighting to help them, give yourself permission not to watch graphic footage of animal cruelty, especially at times when you feel it may impact your mood. Know that you are already creating a kinder world for animals, and that they need you to be strong.

• Focus on the positives: Avoid entering into unproductive conversations and focus your energy on discussions where you can engage positively, such as offering your support and advice to someone trying plant-based food. If you're a social media user, opt for groups that promote friendly discussion and pages that advocate in a positive way. I also recommend following some animal sanctuaries for a daily dose of happy rescued animals.

• Set boundaries: Setting boundaries that help you to take care of yourself as an advocate will be different for each person. You might find that turning off social media for a few hours before bed helps you to switch off from animal issues. Maybe you need to give yourself permission not to advocate with a particular family member in order to avoid repeating unproductive conversations. Have a think about boundaries that will help you stay happy and healthy and allow you to put them into effect.

• Visit an animal sanctuary: Spending time with the animals we fight for, who are living the life all animals deserve, can be just what we need to remind us that the world is full of compassion, kindness and hope, if we just remember to look for it.

• Recharge: Feeling burnt-out or overwhelmed? Carve out some time to surround yourself with the people who love and support you, or recharge your batteries by doing an activity you love. If you need some additional support, seek the help of a professional. Know that it's okay to take a break. Your wellbeing is important.

REMEMBER, YOU ARE AMAZING

Every time you choose a plant-based meal, you spare animals from cruelty, and help create a greener planet. Every conversation you have with someone can be the beginning of their journey to a kinder way of eating and living.

The number of people choosing plant-based meals and the number of plant-based options in restaurants and supermarkets continues to grow every day. Take time to reflect on this progress and the important role you are playing in making it possible.

Thanks for being part of the movement. We've got this!

WHY I WENT VEGAN
by Andrew

I was a bigger meat eater than most until around 12 years ago, when a conversation with a slaughterhouse worker in a pub changed things for me. She was responsible for bolt-gunning cows in the head, which is supposed to render them unconscious. Time pressure means that they aren't always accurate with the bolt gun and they don't have time for a second shot if they miss. She told me that the accepted industry standard was that eight out of ten cows should be effectively 'stunned' before progressing down the production line but, in reality, the figure was closer to six or seven out of ten. This meant that three or four out of every ten cows had their throats slit and were hung up by their back leg to bleed out while fully conscious and screaming and thrashing around in pain (I didn't even know cows could scream until I saw this on video, it's tattooed on my brain) because the 'merciful' bolt-gun missed their brain beforehand.

She seemed like a really lovely person, which made her honest revelations even more confronting to me. As this conversation sunk in over the next few days, I imagined myself in the position of these animals and allowed the full weight of reality to sit on my shoulders and in my heart. It dawned on me that no matter what I told myself about my love for animals and my wishes for a peaceful world, I had undoubtedly paid for a cow (many cows) to have its skin removed while fully conscious and screaming in pain. Was my enjoyment of a good burger really worth all the pain and suffering? Most of us would agree that it's best to avoid unnecessary violence, and this conversation convinced me that I needed to find a way to remove myself from the equation. I no longer wanted to support this misery and horror by paying people to do these things on my behalf. My only regret is that I didn't make this decision sooner.

KLAUS MITCHELL

I was blessed to be able to meet and party with Klaus at the Healthy Lifestyle Expo in LA during my year of potatoes. He was there to document the event for 'Plant Based News' and I had the honour of being interviewed by him for his website. He is driven and dedicated to making important information about the plant-based diet and lifestyle available and accessible to the masses. He has created many viral videos and other stories that help this message reach so many people who would otherwise remain oblivious to the myriad of benefits on offer to people willing to open their minds to the idea of change.

As the founder of 'Plant Based News', he's so much more than a journalist; he's the driving force behind one of the fastest-growing websites around. He's a keen student of science, which is plainly obvious to anyone who has watched his insightful conversations with many of the world's foremost nutrition and health researchers.

He's also another man after my own heart, who prefers to keep his fuel simple and occupy his mind with more important things, like world domination for the plant-based lifestyle!

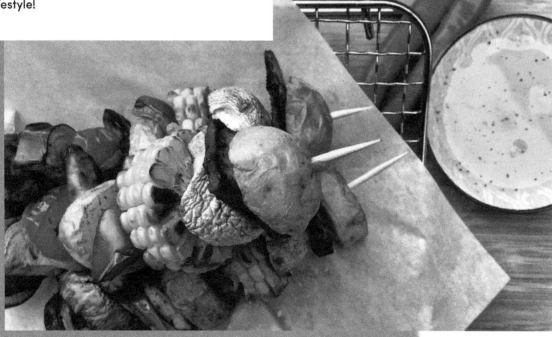

MARINATED TOFU, POTATO + VEGETABLE KEBAB <u>w</u> SPICY PINEAPPLE SALSA

¶¶¶¶¶¶

I like this recipe because it is essentially simple: veggies on a stick on a grill. Pre-mixed Caribbean spices make the marinade really easy, but I've included the separate ingredients in case you can't find one or just want to make it yourself. Any herb or spice mix you like will work with this, and so will any veggies, but potatoes and sweetcorn are two of my personal favourites. Makes 3 kebabs

150 g (5½ oz) firm tofu, cut roughly into 6 chunks
1 small eggplant (aubergine), cut roughly into 6 chunks
1 zucchini (courgette), cut into 6 chunks
3 small-medium potatoes, cut into 3 pieces each, then boiled or steamed
1 red capsicum (bell pepper), cut roughly into 6 chunks
6 button mushrooms
1 large corn cob, cut into 6 segments (or 2 smaller cobs cut into thirds)
6 cherry tomatoes
Marinade
2 tablespoons lemon juice
1 tablespoon pineapple juice
1½ tablespoons tamari
½ teaspoon onion powder
½ teaspoon garlic powder
2 teaspoons Caribbean spice mix, or see recipe below
Caribbean spice mix
½ teaspoon French mustard
¼ teaspoon ground turmeric
¼ teaspoon paprika
¼ teaspoon ground cardamom
¼ teaspoon ground cumin
¼ teaspoon cayenne pepper
¼ teaspoon freshly ground black pepper

Pineapple salsa
1 x 225 g (8 oz) tin unsweetened pineapple, drained
2 teaspoons lemon juice
½ teaspoon finely chopped red chilli
¼ teaspoon garlic powder
pinch of salt

First, marinate the tofu. Combine all the marinade ingredients in a bowl and mix well. Toss the cubed tofu in the marinade, then cover and leave to marinate for 2–3 hours or preferably overnight.

If you are using wooden skewers, soak them in a bowl of cold water while you prepare the veggies. This will stop them from burning when grilled.

Lightly steam the eggplant and zucchini in a steamer basket suspended over a saucepan of boiling water, about 2 minutes.

In a large mixing bowl, combine all the veggies and tofu. Add 125 ml (4 fl oz/½ cup) water to the leftover marinade, mix, then add to the mixing bowl. Toss gently to coat the vegetables.

Arrange the vegetables on the skewers in whatever order you prefer: 3 pieces of potato and 2 pieces each of everything else on each skewer. Avoid squashing them too close together or they won't cook properly.

Heat a grill or barbecue to high heat and grill until the veggies are soft and slightly charred, turning regularly.

Serve with a drizzle of the pineapple salsa.

NATASHA & LUCA
THAT VEGAN COUPLE

Natasha and Luca are on a mission to make the right choice the easy choice. For a long time, they lived the stereotypical Western lifestyle, centred around climbing the corporate ladder in order to get more money to buy more stuff they didn't need and letting their health suffer along the way.

In their darkest hour, they found comfort in the words 'leap and the net will appear'. What followed was a major shift in consciousness and lifestyle. Their fulfilling life of minimalism, yoga, clean, sober living and vegan activism is a far cry from their former lives, and through their YouTube channel and their podcast they share what they've learned in their own transformations to create a happier, healthier life and planet for all of us and for the animals.

POTATO NACHOS

Ͳ Ͳ Ͳ Ͳ Ͳ Ͳ

First and foremost, we love this recipe because it's based on potatoes! Other than that, it's delicious, fast and easy to make. Like most other people, we're always so busy and just don't have time to spend in the kitchen working out long recipes. The other thing we love is that this version of nachos is actually healthy for you. We used to love eating nachos, but always felt so sick afterwards. With this meal, you can still enjoy the tasty nacho toppings, but enjoy a healthy base of baked spuds instead of corn chips. Serves 1

3 medium potatoes
handful chopped coriander (cilantro), to serve
Toppings
½ small red onion, diced
2 tomatoes, chopped
80 g (2¾ oz) corn kernels
80 g (2¾ oz) black beans
2 teaspoons paprika
1 teaspoon mixed herb and garlic seasoning
1 tablespoon vegan yoghurt (optional)
1 tablespoon tomato ketchup (optional)
1 tablespoon sweet chilli sauce (optional)
½ avocado, smashed (optional)

Wash the potatoes and cut them into large wedges. You can cook the potatoes a couple of different ways:

Preheat the oven to 250°C (480°F).

Option 1

Place the potatoes in a large saucepan, cover with cold water and bring to the boil over a high heat. Boil for 8 minutes, then drain and transfer to a baking tray. Cover the tray with foil, reduce the temperature to 200°C (400°F) and bake for 30–40 minutes.

Once the potatoes are almost cooked, remove the foil and bake for a further 10 minutes to crisp up.

Option 2

Skip the boiling stage of option 1.

Place the cut potatoes straight on a baking tray, cover with foil and bake for 1 hour.

Once the potatoes are almost cooked, remove the foil and bake for a further 10 minutes until golden and slightly crispy.

To prepare the toppings, heat a little water in a large frying pan and sauté the onion. Add the chopped tomato, corn and black beans and stir to mix well. Add the spices and stir until well combined.

Cover the pan, reduce the heat to low and simmer for 5–10 minutes.

Transfer the cooked potatoes to a serving plate and top them with the topping mixture.

We like to serve our nachos with vegan yoghurt, ketchup and sweet chilli sauce, and you can add some smashed avocado for an authentic nachos taste.

Garnish with fresh cilantro/coriander if desired.

Note
You can use dried black beans if you prefer, just remember to soak them overnight and cook them until soft in boiling, salted water first.

VEGAN EASY

I really believe all the problems of the world can be solved with education. We humans are overwhelmingly good, kind-hearted people who are doing the best we can with the information we have. What we need more than anything is for information to flow freely so that the masses are able to make properly informed decisions that align with their own moral compass. People want to do good – they just need to know how and it helps if it's easy!

'VeganEasy.org' has helped hundreds of thousands of people open their hearts and minds to veganism as a simple and effective choice they can make to save the lives of animals, live healthily and lighten their eco-footprint. Their '30-Day Vegan Challenge' supports and motivates new vegans by showing them how easy and delicious vegan food can be, while providing free help and resources to people already on their journey towards veganism.

Maya Angelou said 'Do the best you can until you know better. Then, when you know better, do better'.

POTATO TORNADOS

These spiralised potato tornados pack a big cheesy punch, and the seasoning can be adapted according to your taste. Don't stress if your spirals aren't perfect first go – it gets easier with practice!
Makes 4 tornados

4 medium, well-shaped white, purple or sweet potatoes
15 g (½ oz/¼ cup) nutritional yeast
40 g (1½ oz/¼ cup) cashew nuts
½ teaspoon smoked paprika
½ teaspoon garlic powder
½ teaspoon onion powder
½ teaspoon dried Italian herbs
sea salt and freshly ground black pepper
chopped coriander (cilantro) or flat-leaf (Italian) parsley, to serve
sauce of your choice, to serve (optional)

Preheat the oven to 210°C (410°F) and line a baking tray with baking paper.

Skewer the potatoes on firm metal skewers. Take a small, sharp knife and, starting from one end of the potato, cut around it in a circular motion to create a spiral. Once finished, separate the spirals on the skewer so that they resemble the image here (it may also be handy to look at a YouTube video on how to do this if you get stuck). Repeat with the remaining potatoes.

Combine the nutritional yeast and cashews in a blender and blitz until well combined. Transfer the mixture to a bowl and add the spices. Season to taste with salt and pepper.

Cover your spiralled potatoes with the seasoning. (It helps if they are moist so the mixture sticks to the potatoes.)

Bake for 45 minutes, or until golden and soft. Turn every 20 minutes or so until all sides are evenly browned.

Serve with coriander and sauce of your choice for dipping.

JAMES ASPEY

Before starting my year of potatoes, I was pretty sure it couldn't be done. I thought it would just be too difficult, too mentally challenging for me to stick to eating only potatoes for an entire year. James Aspey was someone who inspired me to at least give it a shot! A couple of years earlier, James went for an entire year without speaking, while travelling around the country on his bike to raise awareness for the voiceless victims of animal agriculture. Not speaking for an entire year seemed much harder than eating only potatoes, so I thought to myself 'If James can do that, then I can do this!'. Over the course of his year, he drew widespread attention to the plight of animals and has since become a tireless full-time activist, speaker and promoter of peace. James started out with his focus on reducing the suffering of animals in the farming system, and without realising or intending it, he played a huge role in my success too. It's a true honour to now call him a friend.

CINNAMON—SPICED SWEET POTATO PANCAKES

Ⓨ Ⓨ Ⓨ Ⓨ Ⓨ Ⓨ

If you can find an easier pancake recipe that is this delicious, it would be a miracle! It's sweet, filling, fast, and cheap. They're also totally healthy – healthy enough to become and can be a regular part feature of your mornings... or evenings... or midnight snacks... or any meal, really. Serves 2

2 large, very ripe, bananas
½ baked sweet potato
375 g (13 oz/3 cups) rolled oats
500 ml (17 fl oz/2 cups) soy, almond milk or
 other plant-based milk of your choice
pinch of ground cinnamon
fresh fruit, to serve

Combine all the ingredients in a blender and blitz until smooth. You may need to add a little more milk if the batter is too thick. Allow the mixture to sit for 2 minutes.

Heat a large, non-stick frying pan over a medium heat and dollop 2 heaped tablespoons of batter into the pan and spread it out into a pancake. Fill the pan with as many pancakes as you can at a time.

When the edges of the pancakes lift slightly, flip them over with a spatula and fry on the other side until golden brown.

Top with fresh fruit, and serve.

WELLNESS WARRIORS

The people in this chapter might be the most important of all. These are the people next door, the people who don't necessarily have a piece of paper to show or letters after their names. These are people who share from their own personal experiences more than anything else, and they are the people we can all relate to because they've had their struggles and their desires to find a better way to live. They have all found a way to become healthier, better, more complete people than they were yesterday. They are not founts of knowledge, but they're doing what they can to find answers to the questions we all have, and they want us to come along for the ride. Best of all, they lead in the only way that truly matters: by example. They fearlessly share their successes and failures in the hope that we can all learn from them, and they have a lot of fun doing it!

BROCCOLI CHEDDAR SOUP

I like this recipe because its super easy, quick and delicious. And just like 'traditional' broccoli cheddar soup, it's very filling and comforting too! Serves 2

3 russet potatoes, peeled and chopped
180 g (6½ oz/3 cups) broccoli florets
1 teaspoon garlic powder
1 teaspoon onion powder
1 teaspoon bouillon powder
30 g (1 oz/½ cup) nutritional yeast

Combine all the ingredients, except the nutritional yeast, with 750 ml (25½ fl oz/3 cups) water in a large saucepan. Bring to the boil, then reduce the heat, cover and simmer for 20 minutes, or until the potatoes are soft.

Add the nutritional yeast, then transfer half the soup to a blender and blitz until smooth. Add it back to the remaining soup and mix well.

HANNAH JANISH
HIGH CARB HANNAH

A couple of weeks into my year of spuds, I was told about High Carb Hannah's own 'potato cleanse'. Turned out, this huge YouTuber was halfway through her own potato-based diet, where she was eating only potatoes along with non-starchy veggies. While not exactly the same, it was so exciting to see that there was a whole movement building at the time with a bunch of people coming to realise and experience in their own way the incredible benefits of the humble spud. Hannah had a pretty awesome experience with her 'potato cleanse' and, in the process, has shown her legions of followers how we can benefit from simplicity while still eating beautiful, delicious food.

Hannah has lost over 31 kg (70 lb) since adopting a whole food, plant-based diet and now writes books and spends her time inspiring countless others through her YouTube channel to change their lives with help from the humble spud.

JOSH LAJAUNIE

I cried my eyes out listening to Josh LaJaunie talk about his experiences losing over 90 kg (200 lb) by switching to a whole food, plant-based diet and running. He really hit the nail on the head with his description of 'falling out' with the foods that had taken him to 180 kg (400 lb) and beyond. He understood that no matter how much he loved the traditional foods of his home in South Louisiana, they didn't love him back, and they weren't going to help him get to where he wanted to be. His relationship with food was dysfunctional, and it simply couldn't go on that way.

Incremental changes led him to lose the first 45 kg (100 lb) and began his love affair with running. Changing to a fully whole food, plant-based diet helped him lose the next 45 kg (100 lb) and become a legitimate athlete in his own right, having been featured on the cover of 'Runner's World' magazine! A proud 'coonass', Josh's love and compassion for the 'bayou

brethren' who share his struggles has led him on a mission to change the way people think and feel about food and, more importantly, about themselves. His 'Missing Chins Run Club' has been a bottomless pit of inspiration and motivation in my own journey.

As you can see from the utter simplicity in Josh's recipe, he's clearly a man after my own heart. He sums it up best in his 'Free Josh LaJaunie Manifesto': 'I look forward to spreading the word about how doable and necessary it is for us to adopt a naturally human lifestyle, which I believe is eating plants to fuel physical excursion'.

DECONSTRUCTED POTATO SALAD

The reason I prefer my tater salad deconstructed is twofold:
1. It's easy to do on the go; grab a tater, throw on the accoutrements, and boom! Out the door.
2. It really resonates with being a proponent of a whole food, plant-based diet. It's a small, symbolic thing, but it always feels good to think that Essy (Dr Caldwell Esselstyn) and Dr Campbell (T. Colin Campbell) might be proud of me if they saw me eating this.. Serves 1

1 baked potato, thickly sliced
2 teaspoons mustard
2 teaspoons pickle relish
sea salt and freshly ground black pepper

Spread the potato slices out on a serving plate, dollop on some mustard and pickle relish and season to taste with salt and pepper.

Each little slice is like a potato salad being created inside your mouth as you chew.

CHANA MASALA POTATO PIZZA

Pizza is a rich source of comfort calories, and this potato-crust hack fits the bill without refined flours or delivery drivers. You keep your calorie density lower than refined flour and enjoy all your favorite veggie toppings. Adding an Indian flair with chana masala pairs extremely well with the potato crust, almost like an Indian dosa, but you can use any toppings you like, just keep the liquid level low or the sauce thick! Serves 2

Crust
4 russet potatoes (or any variety)
plant-based milk of your choice (almond works well, but pay attention that is it not vanilla or sweetened, as that will ruin it!)
Topping
1-2 cloves garlic, finely chopped or crushed (optional)
½ brown onion, chopped (optional)
1 tomato, chopped

250 ml (8½ fl oz/1 cup) tomato passata (puréed tomatoes)
½ teaspoon ground turmeric
½ teaspoon ground coriander
1 inch piece fresh ginger, finely chopped
1 x 400 g (14 oz) tin chickpeas
1 red capsicum (bell pepper), finely chopped
1 small yellow pumpkin (squash), finely chopped
1 small zucchini (courgette), finely chopped
rosemary leaves, to garnish
sea salt, to taste
½ bunch spring onions (scallions), to garnish

Preheat the oven to 180°C (350°F).

Peel and boil the potatoes, then mash, but don't over-do it. Add enough milk, 1 tablespoon at a time, to achieve a malleable consistency – not so wet that it turns to mush, but not so dry that it's brittle.

Line a baking tray with baking paper and scoop the potato mixture onto it. Shape it into a circular pizza 'crust' and bake for 15 minutes, or until brown. If you need to, increase the heat a little so that it browns. Flip the crust over and bake for another 15 minutes on the other side. To flip it, simply slide the crust, baking paper and all off the tray, place a fresh sheet of baking paper down, then flip the crust face-down on top and peel off the old baking paper.

To make the topping, heat a frying pan over a medium heat and sauté the onion and garlic, if using, in a little water. Add the chopped tomato and passata reserving some fresh tomato to top the pizza if desired.

Add the spices, ginger and chickpeas, and bring to the boil. Cook until sauce thickens, about 5–10 minutes.

Top the pizza crust with the tomato sauce and scatter over the capsicum, pumpkin and zucchini. Bake for 10–15 minutes, ensuring the crust doesn't burn but the vegetables are cooked.

Garnish with the rosemary leaves, salt and a scattering of spring onion. Slice and serve the pizza with a spatula and fork – it doesn't hold together that well, but it's fun to eat!

ALEX & KRISTIN MACDOWELL
MR AND MRS VEGAN

Mr and Mrs Vegan themselves were also at the Healthy Lifestyle Expo, where they were very generous with their time and advice for me. They've been living the 'whole starch, low fat' lifestyle for longer than most, and have many unique insights and strategies (and recipes!) for making this lifestyle work. Their YouTube channel is a veritable treasure trove of scientific reviews, recipes and tips for making all parts of a healthy lifestyle change as easy as possible. They really do cover all aspects, from science, cooking, a habit and mind set change, to travelling and partying in style. Best of all, they make it fun and accessible, showing how simple, cheap and easy it can be to live and eat in a way that allows us to reach the peak of our powers.

The idea to 'quit food' for a year was preceded by a late-night, artery clogging pizza binge of epic proportions, so it's good to know that I can now welcome pizza back into my life!

MESSY VEGGIES

Jaime and Simon are the coolest kids around, and they can help you to level up in that regard too. They know where all the coolest places are and where all the coolest stuff happens around Melbourne, and they're not too cool to share it with you.

Messy Veggies began as a simple passion project to document their personal switch to a vegan lifestyle. Coupled with Simon's coeliac diagnosis, it was important to create and record easy and healthy recipes. It has since morphed into an all-encompassing guide to everything that Melbourne has to offer the vegan community, with the intention to expand to other cities too.

Messy Veggies is your vegan sauce, they go with everything and it's the tastiest part. A cultured vegan guide to your city, through food, fashion, people, recipes, events, education and health.

GARLIC + THYME SWEET POTATOES ᵂ VEGAN PARMESAN

♨♨♨♨♨♨♨

We love this recipe because it doesn't have too many ingredients and we can put it into the oven quickly and forget about it until it's ready. It also doubles as a good replacement for garlic bread as its nice and garlicky, without the white bread, and the vegan parmesan gives it a lovely cheesy flavour.
Serves 4

4 small sweet potatoes

2 cloves garlic, minced

4 sprigs lemon thyme, finely chopped

2 tablespoons water

Vegan Parmesan

1/3 cup cashews

1 tablespoon nutritional yeast

1/2 teaspoon salt

Pre-heat the oven to 200° (390°F).

Slice the potatoes very thinly along their length, being very careful not to cut all the way through so that they are still held together. We use one chopstick on each side to stop the knife from hitting the cutting board.

Combine the garlic and thyme in a small dish with the water.

Place the potatoes on a tray lined with baking paper and brush with the garlic and herb mixture.

Make sure you get in between every slice to distribute the flavours evenly. Bake for 45 minutes or until they have become visibly crispy.

While the potatoes are baking, make the parmesan: place all ingredients in a blender and blitz until combined.

Remove the sweet potatoes from the oven, sprinkle liberally with the parmesan and garnish with the lemon thyme.

SETAREH KHATIBI

Setareh Khatibi is another member of this weird and wonderful potato-eating subculture that I never knew existed until I was in it. The first rule of potato club is to tell everyone about potato club and, with her hugely popular #potatodiet program, she's well and truly earned the right to be a leader.

This multi-talented singer, actor, comedian and nutrition coach is a one-woman show that will have you laughing all the way to health. Setareh is a former reality-show star and beauty contestant who found her way to low-fat, plant-based eating in an effort to heal her polycystic ovaries. This simple change in diet did that and more, and became her way of life in 2013.

Setareh's career and life purpose took a new direction when her mother suffered an unexpected heart attack. Afterwards, she helped her mum make the switch to a starch-based diet through a McDougall 10-day program (see page 19), which saw her lower her cholesterol, control her diabetes and ultimately avoid bypass surgery.

With powerful stories such as these, Setareh feels duty-bound to share what she's learned and show the fun side of healthy eating. She's 'Starch Solution-certified' through Dr McDougall's training program, and has coached countless people from all over the globe to take control of their health with help of the #potatodiet.

PURPLE SWEET POTATO BROWNIES

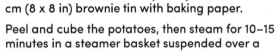

Did you say potatoes AND dessert? Only three ingredients AND it's easy to make? I'm in! This is a totally guilt-free, high-carb, low-fat dessert that guarantees a happy dance every time you bite into it. Not to mention that these brownies are naturally beautiful. It's not often that you'll see purple brownies. It's quite a magical experience for all kids, ages 1–99! Makes 8-12

4–5 small purple (Hawaiian) sweet potatoes
60 g (2 oz/½ cup) carob or cacao powder
360 g (12½ oz/2 cups) pitted, soaked medjool dates or 125 ml (4 fl oz/½ cup) maple syrup
1 teaspoon vanilla extract (optional)

Preheat the oven to 180°C (350°F). Line a 20 x 20 cm (8 x 8 in) brownie tin with baking paper.

Peel and cube the potatoes, then steam for 10–15 minutes in a steamer basket suspended over a saucepan of simmering water, until soft. Drain, and mash.

Put the dates and their soaking water in a food processor and blend until soft. Add the carob powder, vanilla extract, if using, and the mashed potato and blend until well combined.

Pour the mixture into the prepared tin and bake for 45 minutes to 1 hour. Remove the brownies from the oven, turn them onto a rack and allow to cool for 10-15 minutes.

Slice and enjoy!

HOW TO COOK SPUDS &
INFLUENCE PEOPLE

by Andrew

When we've found the solution to our own problems and the problems of the world, we get excited and we want to tell everyone about it so they can experience the same euphoria. This is a totally natural human reaction. We've all got friends and family who are sick, overweight and unhealthy. We know people who are stuck in a rut, struggling with relationships or jobs they aren't happy in. We think 'if only my friend would just try this awesome thing that worked for me, I just know they'd love it!' But alas, we can push, prod, cajole and coax endlessly, but we don't always get through to them.

How can we finally help people start making the changes that we are so sure will help? The wellness warriors in this chapter have the best answer to that question. The answer to changing people is not to focus on changing them at all, but changing ourselves.

I firmly believe that there is not a person alive who doesn't want to improve themselves in one way or another. Not a single person believes that they are the complete and finished product and that there isn't something that could be improved upon. We are all a work in progress, whether we choose to admit it or not. Everyone has changes they want to make in their lives and things they want to improve. Everyone. We are constantly bombarded with people telling us what we should do and how we should do it. We've heard from parents, teachers, politicians, magazine covers and the media exactly how we are failing in our lives and what we should be doing about it.

Your loved ones don't need another nagging voice to listen to. People already know what's wrong with their lives; chances are they already know the solution too (or at least part of it). People don't need advice, they need leaders. They don't need to be told what to do or how to do it, they need to be shown. Some challenges in life just seem so big and scary that they feel insurmountable, so why even bother starting? People need you to show them that the enormous mountain on the horizon can be climbed and that every step of the process will be worth it. You can't singlehandedly transport anyone to the top of that mountain, but you can show them the way to get there, cheer them on and offer a helping hand along the way.

In order to be a good leader, people need to be able to relate to you. They need to recognise a part of themselves in you that will help them to connect on a deeper level. It's all good fun when Olympic gold is won by the illusion of a super athlete with perfect genetics who has never struggled in their life, but nobody is helped by it. When the super athlete opens up and we learn what they've overcome to get there, we feel a connection and we become emotionally invested; it gives us hope. The key is in the vulnerability and the sharing. Ultimately, we can't do anything for anyone else, but we can provide hope for them and we can show them what is possible when thoughts, wishes, hopes and dreams morph into action.

NINA AND RANDA NELSON

The whole Nelson family have been at the forefront of the plant-based movement for a long time. They welcomed me into their home with open arms and took me on a fantastic tour of LA while I was attending the Healthy Lifestyle Expo, which they put together. Nina and Randa were the yoga instructors for the weekend and made me hurt in places where I didn't know I had places!

The twins were already long-time vegans when they suffered a great deal with severe acne all over their faces. After advice from Dr John McDougall (see page 19), they removed all fatty foods from their diet and miraculously watched their acne clear up to the point where they now have beautiful glowing skin with no trace of any acne.

When they aren't busy as singing, songwriting, dancing actors on TV shows like 'Modern Family', they share what they've learned through their huge YouTube channel. Nina and Randa have a lot of fun covering all sorts of topics, with a focus on helping those suffering with acne to achieve the same results as they have. 'The Clear Skin Diet' has already changed many lives in the short time since its release, giving people their confidence back.

CAULI'FREDO SAUCE

Traditional alfredo sauce is made with thick (double/heavy) cream, cheese and butter. It's like a triple-bypass in a saucepan. But not to worry, you can still have a very flavourful white sauce for your pasta, without risk to your heart – or your skin.
Serves 2-4

1 medium cauliflower head
3 teaspoons garlic powder
2 teaspoons onion powder
15 g (½ oz/¼ cup) nutritional yeast
2 tablespoons lemon juice
125 ml (4 fl oz/½ cup) oat milk

Steam the cauliflower until soft in a steamer basket suspended over a saucepan of simmering water.

Combine all the ingredients in a blender and blitz until smooth and creamy. Reheat as necessary and serve with pasta.

SANDY PLUSS

Sandy Pluss is relatively unusual (at least for this book) in that she didn't arrive at whole food, plant-based eating through any sort of personal health crisis or professional obligation to help others get healthy. She just wanted to learn more about nutrition and good health. In the process of educating herself, she read a couple of books that changed her life. One was 'Turn Off The Fat Gene' by Neal Barnard, and the other was 'Skinny Bitch'. Soon after, she changed her own diet and has been showing people how delicious and healthy plants can be ever since. I can't relate at all to this story; I don't understand how someone can change their habits like this without first experiencing some form of extreme pain that makes the prospect of continuing on down the same road unbearable. But, maybe that's just me!

Seriously though, I really appreciate Sandy's no-frills attitude to cooking. It doesn't have to look like a magazine cover, it doesn't have to please thousands of devoted Instagram fans, and it doesn't have follow the latest trends. It does have to be straightforward, easy, healthy and hearty. It's so easy to just stop at the local takeaway on the way home after a long day and load up on highly processed garbage night after night. Sandy recognises that if we want to make any real progress, than we need to make the healthy choice the easy choice. She wants busy parents to be able to get a dinner on the table that will please the masses with a minimum fuss.

QUICK & EASY POTATO NACHOS

I love these recipes because they are quick & easy, yet wholesome. They are also flavours that aren't too extreme or contain 'exotic' ingredients (read 'weird vegan food'!) and also appeal to the non plant-based eaters!
Serves 4-6

2–4 potatoes
1 onion, finely chopped
1 small capsicum (bell pepper), finely chopped
1 small zucchini (courgette), finely chopped
200 g (7 oz) tinned corn kernels, drained
200 g (7 oz) tinned refried beans
pinch each of paprika, ground cumin and dried oregano
¼ large avocado, or ½ small - mashed
2 tablespoons salsa
2 large handfuls of baby spinach leaves

Thinly slice the potatoes into small rounds. Place on a microwave chip-maker and microwave for 8–12 minutes until you achieve your desired crispness. Check every few minutes as they can burn very easily (see Note).

While the potatoes are cooking, heat a frying pan over medium heat and sauté the onion, capsicum and zucchini until soft, adding small amounts of water to stop the vegies from sticking.

Add the corn, refried beans, spices and salsa. Stir until well combined and heated through, then add the spinach and stir again until wilted.

Serve the bean mixture over the potato 'chips' and top with the mashed avocado.

Note

Microwave chip-makers are available in most homewares stores, or on eBay for a few dollars. If you don't have a microwave, the potato slices can be baked at 200°C/400°F for 30–40 minutes, but obviously this is not quite as 'quick'.

POTATO WAFFLES

Serves 1

1 potato (per waffle)

Place the potatoes in a microwave-safe bowl and cover with water. Microwave on high for 10 minutes. Once cooked, drain and make sure the skin is completely dry. (If you don't have a microwave, you can boil the potatoes until tender, but not falling apart.)

Place a potato in a preheated waffle iron. Make sure the waffle iron is hot before you put the potato in.

Press the lid closed to squash down the potato. Heat for approximately 6–8 minutes per potato. You can press more than one potato at a time if you like. This will depend on the size of the potatoes and your waffle iron.

Do not lift the lid if you think the potato is sticking; it means it's not cooked enough yet. If in doubt, wait a bit longer and they will just get crispier.

My favourite way to enjoy these is with a veggie patty and salad leaves between two potato waffles.

TEGAN STEELE

Tegan is a lover of life, Mother Earth and exploring the wonderful things she has to offer. She eats consciously, thinks positively and has an attitude of gratitude. She's a Swiss Army Knife of wellness, as a talented author, speaker, whole foods, plant-based guru and yogi. She's an entrepreneur with her own beauty line and, in her spare time, she does juice-fasting retreats, cooking classes, women's circles and helps run Urban Projuice, the family, plant-based cafe. Is there anything she can't do?

Apart from being a superhero who has mastered the secrets of time travel (how else could she fit all this in?!), Tegan is a powerful woman who lifts the spirits of those around her with an infectious smile and positive energy. It may seem like a scattergun approach to some, but it is all tied together with her simple personal mission to 'help make the world a healthier place, one person at a time'.

VEGGIE PIE

This vegie pie is one of our family favourites. It tastes best served with the vegan pesto and tomato relish. You can use absolutely any combination of roasted vegetables in this pie. I have written down my favourite combination, however often I just make it with the ingredients I have in the fridge. Serves 6

2–3 potatoes or sweet potatoes, plus 1 large sweet potato, diced, for the filling
100 g (3½ oz/½ cup) brown rice
55 g (2 oz/¼ cup) pearl barley
50 g (1¾ oz/¼ cup) wild rice
4 tablespoons chia seeds
1 eggplant (aubergine), diced
1 onion, diced
1 red and 1 green capsicum (bell pepper), diced
250 g (9 oz) cherry tomatoes
20 g (¾ oz/⅓ cup) nutritional yeast flakes
1 tablespoon sweet chilli sauce
sea salt and freshly ground black pepper
Pine-nut pesto
60 g (2 oz/2 cups, lightly packed) basil leaves
40 g (1½ oz/¼ cup) raw pine nuts
¼ teaspoon sea salt
3–4 teaspoons lemon juice

Preheat the oven to 180°C (350°F). Line a 20 cm (8 in) springform cake tin with baking paper.

Peel, chop and boil the potatoes until tender when pierced with a sharp knife. Drain, and mash.

Bring another saucepan of water to the boil and cook the brown rice, barley and wild rice in the water until al dente, then drain.

Soak the chia seeds in water, stirring constantly, until they expand and thicken.

Combine the eggplant, onion and capsicum in a roasting tin and roast until evenly soft and browned. On a baking tray lined with baking paper, roast the cherry tomatoes until browned. Set aside.

Add the chia seeds, nutritional yeast flakes and sweet chilli sauce to the mash and mix well. Add the roasted vegetables and mix again.

Transfer the mixture to the prepared tin and bake for 30–40 minutes.

While the pie is baking, make the pine-nut pesto. Combine all the ingredients in a food processor and blend to a smooth paste. Transfer to a jar and store in the fridge for up to 5 days.

Serve the pie with a dollop of the pesto on the side.

Note

Did you know that you can make an egg substitute with chia seeds? Simply combine 1 tablespoon chia seeds with 3 tablespoons water and soak, stirring constantly, until the seeds thicken. Use in place of eggs.

POTATO BRUSCHETTA

Being gluten-free from a young age, I missed out on some of my favourite meals. Having an Italian grandfather, I especially loved bruschetta, so I came up with this delicious alternative so that I didn't have to miss out. It's a perfect finger-food dish for parties! Serves 6

2 large, organic potatoes, thickly sliced
4–6 large, organic tomatoes, diced
1 small red onion, finely diced
handful of fresh basil leaves, finely chopped
2 tablespoons apple-cider vinegar
Himalayan pink salt
1 garlic clove

Preheat the oven to 180°C (350°F).

Put the sliced potato on a baking tray lined with baking paper and bake for 15–20 minutes until slightly brown.

While the potato is cooking, combine the tomato, onion and basil in a small bowl. Mix in the vinegar and salt.

Once the potatoes are baked, remove from the oven and rub with the garlic clove. Leave to cool for a few minutes, then top with the tomato mixture to make bruschetta.

CORINNE NIJJER

Corrine is fearless, authentic and irrepressible in her mission to show that no matter how bad things seem, there is always hope. After being diagnosed with multiple sclerosis at just 24 years of age, she resigned herself to a life of managing this terrible disease with no cure in sight. Years spent clinically obese, depressed, chronically fatigued, constipated, living with monthly candida and in constant pain from fibromyalgia meant that life was pretty miserable.

Things went from bad to worse when, a few months before graduating her Social Work degree, an MS relapse left her numb from the waist down. She was utterly terrified of what life would be like but, in the end, hitting rock bottom inspired her to begin taking control of her health.

She went on a long health journey that would change her life completely, from living off cakes, energy drinks and cigarettes, to adopting a low-fat, whole food, vegan diet. She now puts her heart and soul into helping others as a speaker, author, coach and with her fantastic podcast, 'When Life Gives You Lemons, Go Vegan'.

RAINBOW BAKED POTATOES

¶¶¶¶¶¶

This recipe is family favourite not only because it's so delicious but also because it's a great way to get little kids excited to try new vegetables and become involved in cooking and preparing food. Everyone can help and, when little people help pick the dressings on their baked potatoes, they tend to be less fussy and more eager to eat the meal they've helped prepare. Serves 2

4 medium Dutch Cream potatoes
½ cos (romaine) lettuce, finely sliced
¼ purple cabbage, shredded
1 tablespoon hummus or guacamole (see Dr Hadj's recipe on page 23)
juice of 2 limes
200 g (7 oz/1 cup) raw or cooked corn kernels
2 tomatoes, diced
coconut yoghurt, to serve (optional)
2 tablespoons chopped coriander (cilantro), to serve

Preheat the oven to 180°C (350°F).
Pierce the potatoes a few times, then place them on a baking tray lined with baking paper and bake for 45 minutes until tender and the flesh is easily pierced with a sharp knife.
Once baked, cut the potatoes in half and set them on the table with all the toppings to allow people to assemble their own baked potatoes.

STEPPING INTO THE VOID
by Andrew

'I'd love to do it, but I'm worried about an upcoming event.'

'I want to do it, but I'm worried what my friends will think.'

'I wish I could, but I'm not a good cook.'

These are some of the legitimate concerns that I hear all the time from so many different people who are contemplating one form of life change or another. Change is hard, mostly because of the stories we tell ourselves about how hard it's going to be. As soon as we get an idea for a quest, we automatically fast-forward to the uncomfortable or difficult bits. People want the change without the challenge, but I've got news for you folks: if it doesn't challenge you, it doesn't change you!

There's no way you can have all the answers to all the questions and concerns you have about your quest. There's only so much research, learning and preparation you can do before you start. At some point, you have to step into the void and trust that the path will appear beneath your feet. When you approach your quest with good intentions and give it your best effort, answers will come to you when you need them. Ask questions, learn, prepare, plan and then accept that you can't control everything. Whatever will be will be. Ideas without action are pointless, it's time to step into the void.

SWEET POTATO & BEAN BURGERS

This recipe is quick, simple to make and full of all the good stuff. My family loves these in buns with tomato, lettuce, avocado and hummus, or with a side of home-made potato chips and sauce. Makes 5 burgers

1 medium sweet potato
185 g (6½ oz/1½ cups) cannellini beans, drained and rinsed
150 g (5½ oz/1 cup) oat flour, plus extra for forming the patties
1 tablespoon tahini or nut butter, softened
1 teaspoon pure maple syrup
1 teaspoon garlic powder
1 teaspoon onion powder
1 teaspoon sea salt
2 teaspoons dried oregano
freshly ground black pepper
1–2 tablespoons nutritional yeast
45 g (1½ oz/¼ cup) cooked brown rice (or 50 g/1¾ oz/½ cup breadcrumbs)

Preheat the oven to 180°C (350°F).

Pierce the potato a few times, then place on a baking tray lined with baking paper and bake for 40 minutes to 1 hour until tender and the flesh is easily pierced with a sharp knife.

Once cooked, remove the skin from the potato and place the flesh into a large bowl (you can do this the night before if you like).

Add the beans, flour, tahini, maple syrup, spices and nutritional yeast and mash together with a fork. Cover and refrigerate until the mixture is firm enough to mould into burgers, about 15–20 minutes.

The mixture will be soft and wet. Add the brown rice and form the mixture into five patties, adding a little extra flour as needed to stiffen the mixture. Place on a baking tray lined with baking paper and cook for 20 minutes. The burgers should be lightly browned.

TRINA STEELE

Trina's long, hard battle with Crohn's disease was the catalyst for her to take control of her own health and wellbeing. She recognised that the cure was not going to come from a pill, so she got to work on a more natural solution, switching from pharmacy to 'farmacy' for her choice of treatment. She ultimately returned to health on the back of a diet rich in fresh fruits and veggies, and has since made it her mission to help others do the same.

Trina first became a health coach and saw many people regain vibrant health with her help, which inspired her to go bigger in her efforts to share her message. She saw an opportunity to further help her community get healthy by opening Urban Projuice café. There, she shares her love of fresh, unprocessed plant foods and juices, along with plenty of smiles and good times.

LENTIL SPICED PIE

This dish is a family favourite. It's so easy to make, nutritious and delicious. Serves 4

2–3 medium sweet or white potatoes
2 x 400 g (14 oz) tins organic brown lentils, drained and rinsed
185 g (6½ oz/1 cup) cooked quinoa
2 onions, finely diced
6 garlic cloves, finely diced
1 teaspoon ground turmeric
1 x 400 g (14 oz) tin tomatoes
3 tablespoons apple-cider vinegar
2 tablespoons sugar-free tomato chutney
1 tablespoon mild curry paste
2 tablespoons sultanas
Himalayan pink salt and freshly ground black pepper, to taste

Toppings
1 teaspoon nutritional yeast
2 tablespoons sesame seeds, for sprinkling

Preheat the oven to 180°C (350°F).

Wash, peel and roughly chop the sweet potatoes, then place them in a saucepan and cover with cold water. Bring to the boil over a high heat. Drain, then mash.

Heat a saucepan over medium heat and sauté the onion and garlic in a little water until slightly brown. Add the turmeric and cook for 1 minute.

Add all the remaining ingredients and simmer for 5 minutes over a low heat, stirring regularly.

Pour the lentil mixture into a baking dish and layer the sweet potato mash on top. Sprinkle with nutritional yeast and the sesame seeds. Bake for 1 hour, then enjoy.

CHEESY PASTA SAUCE, TWO WAYS

I love these recipes for two main reasons: simplicity and comfort. As a shift worker, sometimes the only thing that saves me from going bonkers on the ward is knowing that I've got a big bowl of cheesy pasta waiting for me in the fridge. Be it on shift for my meal break, or post-shift after a hard day, my cheesy pasta has always got my back. Not to mention, it's super quick and simple to make, and easy to cook in bulk to save for the next few shifts (if it lasts that long!). So, dozens of bowls of pasta and many potatoes later, I'm pleased to share with you two of my favourite cheesy pasta sauce recipes that can be made using simple ingredients found in your pantry and fridge. And they won't cost you an arm and a leg! These two recipes are delicious just simply stirred through your favourite pasta, but they can also be a great base recipe from which you can build you own sauce creations.

The end result? A cruelty free, cheesed-up meal straight out of vegan pasta heaven! I like to stir through some fresh baby spinach and cherry tomatoes with the smoky paprika sauce, while, for the mac 'n' cheese, I can't go past sprinkling a little extra nutritional yeast on top and washing it down with a good glass of red wine. Bon Appétit! Serves 4-6

GEORGINA MANKEY
FIT WITH GEORGIE

Another of the young folks in this book that has me wondering what the hell I was doing with my life 15 years ago! After getting caught up in the typical life of partying and indulgence that many young people go through, Georgie took things a little too far and started battling with her own demons. I admire the strength of character involved in her decision to remove herself from the toxic environments and friendship circles that were edging her further along the path of self-destruction. Anyone who can course-correct in that way, especially with so much societal and peer pressure tugging at them, has my respect.

Through 'Fit With Georgie' she openly shares her struggles and encourages self-care in all its forms. We should all be putting more effort into self-love if we want to be performin g at our best. Of course, some 'cheesy' pasta should be a major part of everyone's self-care regime!

SMOKY PAPRIKA SAUCE
As the name suggests, it's smoky, rich, creamy, nutty, comforting and tangy, with a side of attitude.

80 g (2¾ oz/½ cup) cashew nuts, soaked overnight
500 g (17½ oz) pasta
¼ teaspoon smoked paprika
2 tablespoons nutritional yeast, plus extra to serve
¼–½ teaspoon sea salt
2 teaspoons Dijon mustard
½ teaspoon onion powder
1 teaspoon Worcestershire sauce
250–375 ml (8½–12½ fl oz/1–1½ cups) plant-based milk of your choice
1 large white potato, peeled, chopped and boiled
1 large sweet potato, peeled, chopped and boiled
freshly ground black pepper, to taste

MAC 'N' CHEESE SAUCE

Giving the traditional mac 'n' cheese a run for its money, this recipe is zesty, rich, buttery, nutty, satisfying and simply irresistible.

80 g (2¾ oz/½ cup) cashew nuts, soaked overnight
500 g (17½ oz) pasta
1 tablespoon lemon juice
2 tablespoons nutritional yeast
1½ teaspoons sea salt
1 teaspoon Dijon mustard
1 teaspoon Worcestershire sauce
250–375 ml (8½–12½ fl oz/1–1½ cups) plan-based milk of your choice
1 large white potato, peeled, chopped and boiled
1 large sweet potato, peeled, chopped and boiled
freshly ground black pepper, to taste

Soak your cashews overnight in cold water. I simply pop mine in a cereal bowl, cover them with water and sit them on the windowsill overnight.

Bring a large saucepan of water to the boil and cook your pasta according to the packet instructions. Drain, cover, and set aside.

Choose your sauce, then combine all the ingredients except the potatoes in a high-speed blender with the cashews. Add the cooled potatoes and blitz until well combined, making sure the mixture is free of any lumps.

If you prefer a runnier sauce, you can add a bit more milk until you reach your desired consistency.

Once you've hit your ultimate saucy consistency, season to taste with pepper.

Serve immediately over the pasta and enjoy it, plain and simple, or stir in your favourite fresh veggies to pad it out a bit.

Notes

I store my sauce in a glass jar in the fridge for 4–5 days. When refrigerated, the sauce will thicken. This is just an added bonus because it becomes spreadable! Spread it on a sandwich to spunk things up a little, or dip some fresh-cut veggies in for an afternoon snack. When stirred through hot pasta, or reheated, your sauce will become runny again.

If you're nut free, you can simply omit the cashew nuts. It will still taste deliciously delectable, but won't be as creamy as one prepared with cashew nuts. I haven't tried this recipe with any other nuts, but you could have some fun experimenting with almonds, brazil nuts, walnuts or even hazelnuts. I find cashews to be the creamiest though.

If, like me, you always forget to soak your cashews overnight, you can boil them for about 30 minutes to soften instead.

Any plant-based milk will do. If you're soy-free, try your favourite almond milk, or alternatively, you can replace the milk with water or vegetable stock.

Be cautious not to place hot or boiling substances in your blender; hot things tend to expand and explode when blended at high speeds (I learned this the hard way, more than once!). Sometimes I place my potatoes in the fridge to speed up the cooling process while I prepare the rest of the ingredients.

TERRI EDWARDS

As her joints became increasingly swollen and painful, Terri began to worry that she could be heading down the same path towards disability that her mother had experienced at just 50 years of age. Arthritis was taking over her life and her doctors were only able to offer prescriptions that were not helping symptoms. She took matters into her own hands after watching 'Forks Over Knives' and began following a plant-based diet straight away. She quickly saw improvements and, in a short time frame, was able to free herself from pain and swelling, as well as the harmful side effects of the medication. In addition to resolving her inflamed and painful joints, she also lowered her cholesterol, lost 25 kg (55 lb), cleared up her adult acne and resolved her sleep issues.

Her personal mission to help others arose from this experience, and she now runs the extremely popular website 'Eatplant-based.com'. It's an oasis for those seeking wellness and restored health through plant-based nutrition. But beware that the side effects include radiant health, boundless positivity and the occasional urge to do headstands.

LOADED POTATO SKIN BITES

These loaded potato skin bites are the perfect appetiser for family and social gatherings, or game days. Not only are they beautiful, but they taste AMAZING! Not that long ago, I made about 48 of them, thinking that we would have plenty. It still wasn't enough! Obviously, some folks were coming back for seconds!

This is a healthy, mouth-watering version of the traditional loaded potato. It's drizzled with creamy vegan 'cheese' sauce, sprinkled with smoked paprika and piled high with chives and coriander (cilantro). Completely irresistible! Makes 4

450 g (1 lb) small red or russet potatoes
60–125 ml (2–4 fl oz/¼–½ cup) plant-based milk of your choice
2 tablespoons Low-fat eggless mayo (see below)
1 teaspoon sea salt, or to your taste (I really like black salt)
1 teaspoon garlic powder
1 teaspoon onion powder
1 teaspoon smoked paprika, plus extra to serve
Creamy vegan 'cheese' sauce, for drizzling
½ bunch fresh coriander (cilantro), roughly chopped, to garnish
½ bunch chives, roughly chopped, to garnish
Creamy vegan cheese sauce (see Note)
225 g (8 oz/1 cup) peeled and diced potatoes
25 g (1 oz/¼ cup) diced carrots
40 g (1½ oz/¼ cup) diced onions
50 g (1¾ oz/½ cup) raw cashew nuts, or 30 g (1 oz/½ cup) cooked cannellini beans
4 tablespoons nutritional yeast
1 tablespoon lemon juice

1 teaspoon sea salt
½ teaspoon garlic powder
pinch of paprika
pinch of cayenne pepper
Low-fat eggless mayo
1 x 375 g (13 oz) packet tofu
1 tablespoon sweetener of your choice
1 tablespoon lemon juice or red-wine vinegar
1–1½ tablespoons Dijon mustard
¼ teaspoon sea salt

Preheat the oven to 200°C (400°F).

Pierce the potatoes a few times, place on a baking tray lined with baking paper and bake for approximately 30 minutes, or until tender and the flesh is easily pierced with a sharp knife. Remove and leave to cool.

While the potatoes are cooking, make the cheese sauce. Bring 750 ml (25½ fl oz/3 cups) water to the boil in a saucepan. Add the potatoes, carrots and onion and simmer over a medium heat until the vegetables are tender, about 15 minutes. Drain, reserving 250 ml (8½ fl oz/1 cup) of the cooking water, and transfer the vegetables to a blender.

Add all the remaining ingredients, including the reserved cooking water, and blend until smooth. Set aside. Make the mayo by draining the tofu and squeezing out any excess water between two paper towels. Combine all the ingredients in a blender and blitz until smooth. Store in an airtight container in the refrigerator for up to 2 weeks. Once the potatoes are cool, slice them in half and scoop out the flesh into a mixing bowl, leaving one-quarter of it in the shell.

Add the milk, mayo, salt, pepper, garlic powder, onion powder and smoked paprika to the potato, and mash together using a potato masher or a fork.

Fill the potato skins with mashed potato mixture and drizzle with the cheese sauce. Top with more smoked paprika, the chives and coriander. Serve warm.

Note

You can use this cheese sauce to make chilli cheese fries, nacho cheese dip, mac 'n' cheese, as a topping for steamed broccoli, or anything else that needs a good, creamy cheese sauce. Any leftover sauce can be stored in an airtight container in the refrigerator for up to 2 weeks.

JUNK FOOD IS A PUNISHMENT NOT A REWARD
by Andrew

For most of us, food forms an integral part of the way we celebrate and commiserate. Major life events (and minor ones too!) are centred around food. How often have you told yourself 'I've done so well, I deserve this cake,' or 'I've been working so hard, I've earned this little treat'? We trick ourselves into eating junk food as though it somehow makes our efforts worthwhile. The reality is that junk food doesn't pick us up when we are down, it kicks us.

Junk food doesn't make a good time better either, it numbs our emotions and distracts us from being fully immersed in the good times happening around us. We lose 10 kg (22 lb) and then celebrate by taking the first steps in our undoing!

We've lost the ability to feel emotions and appreciate them for what they are. Down times are a part of life, it's okay to feel sad and it's okay to allow the sadness to linger without looking for the first thing we can stuff in our faces to squash it. We need to learn to see success as its own reward. When we achieve something big, we need to get comfortable revelling in our own greatness instead of rewarding ourselves with food.

The greatest moments of our lives are great because we made them happen, not because someone made a cake.

TESS BEGG

Tess went vegan after deciding that she could no longer support the inherent cruelty of the meat and dairy industries. She soon discovered that not only was it easy to make beautiful and delicious food without animal products, but that it also helped fuel her passion for fitness and health. She launched her popular YouTube and Instagram channels shortly after, and has since been inspiring people the world over to live happy, healthy and active lifestyles with plant foods as the centrepiece.

Tess focuses on sharing simple recipes and workouts in an approachable way that makes it easy for people to get the most out of living a plant-based life.

BLACK BEAN QUINOA CHILLI

A Mexican favourite, Spud-ified! Black bean quinoa chilli is one of my favourite recipes as it's wholesome, great to meal-prep and versatile. Enjoy as a filling in wraps, or stuffed in roasted sweet potatoes or on top of thin crunchy potatoes for healthy, delicious and satisfying potato nachos that will leave you feeling nourished. Potatoes are a great alternative to store-bought tortilla chips for nachos, as those are often loaded with unnecessary sodium and oils. Serves 1

Chilli
Makes 1.25 litres (42 fl oz/5 cups)
1 small brown onion, diced
2 garlic cloves, crushed
2 tablespoons tomato paste (concentrated purée)
2 teaspoons ground coriander
4 teaspoons ground cumin
½ teaspoon dried oregano
½ teaspoon chilli powder
½ teaspoon onion powder
1 x 400 g (14 oz) tin cherry or diced tomatoes
200 g (7 oz/1 cup) uncooked quinoa, rinsed
500 ml (17 fl oz/2 cups) vegetable stock or filtered water
1 x 425 g (15 oz) tin black beans, drained and rinsed
2 tablespoons lemon juice
freshly ground black pepper, to taste
Nachos (1 serve)
6-7 small white potatoes - thinly sliced
Mixed herbs, onion powder, dried oregano or seasoning of choice.
1 bell pepper - diced
5 cherry tomatoes - halved
Handful fresh coriander
Handful fresh lettuce
½ avocado - mashed
2-3 tbsp oil-free hummus (see page 13)

For the nachos, preheat the oven to 250° (480°F).

In a bowl, toss the sliced potatoes in the herbs and spices, then spread out evenly on a tray lined with baking paper. Bake for 20-30 minutes.

For the chilli, heat a large saucepan over a medium heat and sauté the onion and garlic in a little water until lightly browned.

Add the tomato paste and spices and cook until fragrant, then stir through the tomatoes.

Add the quinoa and vegetable stock, stir, and bring to the boil. Cover with a lid and reduce the heat to low. Simmer until the liquid is absorbed and the quinoa is cooked.

Stir in the black beans and lemon juice, then check and adjust the seasoning if needed, adding some black pepper and extra spices to taste.

When the potatoes are golden and crunchy, arrange them on a plate, then add the black bean quinoa chilli, bell pepper, tomato, avocado, hummus and coriander, and enjoy!

WILL KRISKI

Most people probably don't know, but Will Kriskl was actually the inspiration for my 'Spud Fit' name. I was a big fan of him and his 'Potato Strong' YouTube channel where he shares recipes and fitness tips. I really liked his name and, when I had to come up with my own, I wracked my brain for days but nothing resonated. Eventually, I just decided to change the words 'Potato Strong' to two different words that meant the same thing, and 'Spud Fit' was born!

Will lost over 15 kg (35 lb) eating a low-fat, no-oil, plant-based diet, adhering to 'The Starch Solution' by Dr John McDougall (see page 19), all while being a sedentary computer programmer. After experimentation and lots of Googling, Will came up with a variety of simple, quick, tasty comfort-food meals that filled him up while dropping the extra pounds, so he decided to share these recipes with the world.

SHREDDED HASH BROWN OMELETTE

¶¶¶¶¶¶¶

I love this recipe as it reminds me of when I used to eat omelettes on a lazy Sunday morning. Some people make a chickpea omelette, but since I'm 'Potato Strong' I had to make it out of potatoes. This has been my main strategy: take a recipe I liked and tweak it to make it plant-based and much healthier.
Serves 1

5 medium potatoes (I prefer ones with yellow flesh)
optional spices, such as onion powder, garlic powder and seasoning salt
tomato ketchup, to serve
Filling
1 onion, chopped
1 green capsicum (bell pepper), chopped
1 red capsicum (bell pepper), chopped
1 tomato, chopped
handful of baby spinach

Wash and grate the potatoes – it's a good workout! Put them in a strainer and rinse under cold running water. Squeeze out any excess, then transfer the potato to a mixing bowl and add the spices and seasoning of your choice to taste. Mix well.

Heat a waffle iron to the highest setting. If you don't have one, just heat the oven to its highest setting and line a baking tray with baking paper.

Cook the potatoes in the grill, waffle iron, or spread out on the baking tray for 20–30 minutes, or until crispy on both sides (if cooking in the oven, you might have to flip the potatoes a few times while cooking.) The potatoes should become a solid layer and be browned on both sides.

Meanwhile, heat a large frying pan over a medium heat and fry the onion. I like to dry-fry my onions first before adding the other veggies and water in order to bring out the natural sugars of the onions. Add the capsicum for the filling (you can add any veggies you like, mushrooms are also good) in a little water or vegetable stock. If the water evaporates, just add a little more to the pan. When the veggies begin to soften, toss in the spinach and cook for another minute or two until wilted.

When the potatoes are done, you should be able to lift the lid of the grill or waffle iron without anything sticking. Remove the potato layer with a spatula and carefully lay it on a plate. Pile the veggies on one side of the layer and top with the chopped tomato. Flip the other half of the potato layer over the vegetables and enjoy with a dollop of ketchup.

ADAM SUD

Adam came from a long way back to arrive in his current position as a leader of the plant-based wellness movement. He had major struggles with addiction, depression, body dysmorphia and diabetes, and was facing a life of desperation and hopelessness on the streets. He realised in time that the only way out was to ask for help from his parents. With their help, he checked into rehab for an extended stay and soon realised that sobriety was not enough for his health and happiness. He took it upon himself to adopt a whole food, plant-based diet and that was when things really started improving for him.

He told himself, 'If I am the cause of my problems, then I get to be the solution'. Within six months, he completely reversed his type-2 diabetes and high blood pressure, and within 1 year, he had lost over 45 kg (100 lb) and was off all the medication he was prescribed in rehab, including anti-depressants, mood stabilisers, sleeping medication and ADHD medication. The change was a struggle at times, but he told himself that if he wanted to change his life he needed to 'be comfortable being uncomfortable until he fell in love with the new lifestyle'. Success is about finding the joy in owning your health and wellbeing.

As of today, he has lost 77 kg (170 lb) and is the happiest and healthiest he has ever been. He believes recovery is the search for the authentic self, and today he is as close as he has ever been to his authentic self. He will tell you that the simplest change on your fork can make the most profound change to your life.

PURPLE SWEET POTATO CINNAMON OATMEAL

Ŧ Ŧ Ŧ Ŧ Ŧ Ŧ

I love this recipe! My two favourite foods are sweet potatoes and oatmeal, so I thought to myself one day, why not combine them into one amazing meal and see what happens? I use the purple sweet potatoes for a couple of reasons: the first because I really love them, and the second is their amazing colour. It is beautiful and fun.

It's exciting to create something that is vibrant, colourful, delicious and healthy all at the same time. It's also important to be excited by what is on your plate. This will help you fall in love with the lifestyle. Because, no matter how healthy you become while living this lifestyle, if you don't love it, you probably won't stick with it. This recipe is full of not just healthy, whole, intact carbohydrates, but also vitamins, antioxidants, water, fibre and minerals. These are the micronutrients that restore and sustain optimal health. I love it, and I hope you will too. Serves 1

110–220g (4–8 oz) purple (Hawaiian) sweet potato, sliced
125 g (4½ oz/1 cup) rolled oats
½ teaspoon ground cinnamon
handful of blueberries and raspberries, to serve

Cut the purple sweet potato into slices

Place the sweet potato in a saucepan and cover with cold water. Bring to the boil over a high heat and cook for 10–12 minutes, or until soft.

Put the oats in another small saucepan. Remove the sweet potato slices from the water, then pour the cooking water on top of the oats. It should be purple from boiling the sweet potato.

Heat the oats over a medium–low heat, stirring constantly, until cooked and creamy. Pour into a bowl and mix in the sweet potato slices. This will also help to thicken up the oatmeal.

If you prefer thinner oatmeal, just add a little extra hot water. Finish with the cinnamon and fresh berries.

ANTHONY MASIELLO

At 6'4" and 163 kg (360 lb), Anthony felt quite comfortable with where his life was at. He couldn't buy clothes in normal shops, he needed heavy-duty seats in his house, and a seatbelt extension when he flew on planes. He was OK with all of that because, in his mind, he was just a guy who was bigger than everyone else – no big deal.

Then, he received a letter to say that he'd been denied life insurance. The insurance company had run the numbers and decided that it was unlikely he'd be alive in 20 years, therefore it wasn't worth their risk to insure him. This came as a rude shock to a 33-year-old fella who thought he was in his prime, but even that wasn't enough to spark change.

When he wasn't allowed on a 'Thomas the Tank Engine' ride with his son because he wouldn't fit, he knew that enough was enough. He switched to a whole food, plant-based diet and, in 20 months lost 72 kg (160 lb), reversed a series of medical conditions and completely transformed his life.

Anthony now lives a healthy and incredibly active life with his wife Cathy and their two sons, Evan and Henry. Since regaining his own health, Anthony has developed a passion for helping others to do and sustain the same. He believes the only path to achieving optimal health is to earn it.

CHICK PEA POTATO CURRY ᵂ KALE

Our family used to love going out for Indian food, but for some reason our kids were never excited about the dishes we tried to make at home, until we came up with this one! We realized that the missing component was sweet potatoes - apparently, our kids love any dish that includes sweet potatoes, and so this chickpea sweet potato curry with kale was born! This dish has been a real crowdpleaser with our family and friends ever since. With the combination of hearty, healthy, wholesome, ingredients, it's a delicious dish that we are proud to serve and share. We hope you enjoy it too! Serves 4-6

3 x 400 g (14 oz) tins chickpeas, rinsed and drained (reserve liquid)
2 medium brown (yellow) onions, diced
4 cloves garlic, minced
4 teaspoons ground cumin
4 teaspoons curry powder
4 teaspoons garam masala
1 teaspoon chilli powder
½ teaspoon cayenne pepper (to taste)
¼ cup water
4 medium sweet potatoes, cubed
2 x 400 g (14 oz) tin diced tomatoes (preferably fire-roasted), blended smooth
225 g (1 ½ cups/8 oz) fresh or frozen green peas
1 bunch kale, chopped

In a food processor or blender purée one can of chickpeas until you achieve a thick, hummus-like consistency, using the reserved liquid as needed.

Sauté the onions and garlic in a large pot with approximately ¼ cup of water. Add more water as needed to prevent sticking.

When the onions are translucent, add all of the seasonings and mix well. Add another ¼ cup of water to create a paste-like consistency.

Add the sweet potatoes, tomatoes, peas, whole chickpeas, and the chickpea puree.

Bring everything to a simmer and cook for 25 minutes, until the sweet potatoes have softened.

Stir in kale, and cook for another 5 minutes.

Serve and enjoy!

BEN LOAKER

When I travelled to Adelaide for a couple of speaking events, Ben and Louise didn't know me at all, but they kindly offered to put me up at their house for a few nights. Ben convinced me to join him in the Adelaide Hills for a few hours on his son's race bike. What followed was a really great afternoon of scenery and conversation, combined with torture and triumph on some of the toughest climbs around.

Ben is a serious, elite-level cyclist and personal trainer, but a visit to the doctor to check out his health proved that exercise alone just doesn't cut it. He had high blood pressure, cholesterol and triglycerides and was quickly progressing down the road to

gout, heart disease and other chronic health issues. The last thing he wanted was to get stuck taking pills for the rest of his life, so he decided to watch 'Forks Over Knives' after a recommendation from a friend. He was totally shocked at what this documentary revealed to him and, along with Louise, they swapped to a whole food, plant-based diet that day. Fast forward and not only have all his blood numbers normalised, but his performance on the bike is going from strength to strength. He now encourages his clients and other athletes to give plants a try and see for themselves the amazing impact they can have on their life and their health. Just do it.

CRUNCHY CURRIED POTATOES

♈ ♈ ♈ ♈ ♈ ♈

This oil-free crunchy, spicy potato dish is always a firm favourite in our house. The sweet potato is a great addition, and makes it stand out from other curried potato dishes. **Serves 2**

1 teaspoon ground turmeric
600 g (1 lb 5 oz) sweet potatoes
2 tablespoons brown-rice flour
3 tablespoons garam masala
1 teaspoon paprika
½ teaspoon cumin seeds
1 teaspoon garlic powder
3 tablespoons soy sauce or tamari
juice of 1 lemon, plus extra to serve
1 large onion, finely diced
2 teaspoons white or black mustard seeds

Preheat the oven to 200°C (400°F).

Bring a saucepan of water to the boil and add the turmeric. Leaving the skin on the potatoes, dice them and add to the water. Boil for 8 minutes, then drain.

Return the potatoes to the saucepan and sprinkle over the brown-rice flour, garam masala, paprika, cumin seeds and garlic powder. Mix well, being quite heavy-handed with the mixing so that you 'rough up' the potatoes a bit. This is what makes them crispy when cooking.

Add the soy sauce, lemon juice and diced onion and mix again. Spread the potatoes out in a single layer on a baking tray lined with baking paper. Roast for 40–50 minutes, mixing a couple of times during cooking to ensure they are browning evenly.

Serve on their own with a squeeze of lemon, as a side dish or with a big green salad.

If you have any leftovers the next day, try stuffing them cold into a wholemeal pita bread. (I always make extra so I can do this.)

CHERIE TU
THRIVING ON PLANTS

Cherie's Instagram feed is the epitome of 'eating the rainbow'; it's overloaded with vibrancy and positivity. Energy and vitality are the inevitable by-products of eating the way she does. As a 19-year-old, I wasn't at all focussed on my health and wellbeing, let alone that of the planet and the rest of its inhabitants. I find it refreshing and comforting to see Cherie using her creativity and skill to help inspire the next generation to lead more conscious lives, starting with what's on their plates.

Plant-based eating is seen as boring by the vast majority of people, but Cherie is doing an amazing job of changing that. I defy anyone to take a look at her amazing creations and then tell me that 'thriving on plants' is boring!

CHILLI STUFFED POTATOES

♉♉♉♉♉♉

This hearty and satisfying recipe is an absolute crowd-pleaser and is bound to become one of your weekly staples. It also makes enough servings for you to store away and enjoy throughout the week for lunch or dinner. I personally love this recipe, as it is easy to make yet brings the regular baked potato to the next level. It's loaded with a decent serving of veggies and beans, and always leaves me feel so satiated! Serves 4

4 medium potatoes
1 onion, diced
1 garlic clove, minced
1 large carrot, diced
1 celery stalk, diced
1 red capsicum (bell pepper), diced
1 x 400 g (14 oz) tin black beans, drained and rinsed
1 x 400 g (14 oz) kidney beans, drained and rinsed
1½ tablespoons chilli powder
½ tablespoon smoked paprika
½ tablespoon ground cumin
½ tablespoon dried mixed herbs
1 x 400 g (14 oz) tin diced tomatoes
60 g (2 oz/¼ cup) tomato paste (concentrated purée)
1 vegetable stock cube
guacamole and cashew cream, to serve (optional)
To garnish
corn kernels
cherry tomatoes, quartered
coriander (cilantro)
squeeze of lime

Preheat the oven to 200°C (400°F).

Pierce the potatoes a few times, then place on a baking tray lined with baking paper and bake for 50 minutes, or until tender and the flesh can be easily pierced with a sharp knife.

In the meantime, heat a large saucepan over a medium–high heat. Once hot, add the onion, garlic, carrot, celery and capsicum and sauté in a little water for 7–8 minutes, or until soft and translucent.

Add the black beans, kidney beans and spices and mix well, then cook for 1 minute.

Mix in the tomatoes, tomato paste, stock cube and 500 ml (17 fl oz/2 cups) water. Bring to the boil, then reduce the heat to low, cover with a lid and simmer gently until thickened (by which time, the potatoes will have cooked).

Remove the potatoes from the oven, slice them in half lengthways and split open using two forks. Spoon the chilli inside each potato and serve with guacamole and cashew cream, if desired. Garnish with corn, coriander, cherry tomato and lime.

Serve immediately while warm.

JACKSON FOSTER
PLANTRIOTIC

Starting my own YouTube channel opened up a whole new world to me that I was previously unaware of. Jackson's 'Plantriotic' channel was one that inspired me to be more open, honest and authentic in what I chose to share with the world. He started his channel to help him document the process of overcoming an eating disorder that had left him underweight and sick. Fast forward a few years, and he is a new man with a new body and a healthy relationship with food. He's on a mission to cycle around the globe fuelled only by whole plant foods. One thing that hasn't changed though is the inspiring way that he shares the trials and tribulations of his nomadic wanderings with so many people.

SWEET POTATO BANANA SMOOTHIE

This recipe comes in handy when you need a hearty meal but only have time for a quick blend. When you're trying to eat healthily, this recipe has you covered. Banana smoothies are a classic choice, but don't always satisfy people as a dinner meal. Blend bananas with baked sweet potatoes and the extra starches will give you longer-lasting energy and deep satisfaction. The frozen bananas also make the smoothie fluffy, like a milkshake.
Makes 1 litre (34 fl oz/4 cups)

1 medium sweet potato
3 bananas, peeled and frozen
3 medjool dates or 5 smaller dates, pitted
375 ml (12½ fl oz/1½ cups) almond milk or other plant-based milk of your choice
1 tablespoon hemp seeds
1 teaspoon ground cinnamon
½ teaspoon vanilla extract
½ teaspoon ground turmeric (optional)

Preheat the oven to 220°C (430°F).

Slice the sweet potato into 2.5 cm (1 in) thick discs and place them on a baking tray lined with baking paper. Bake for 30 minutes, or until soft but not blackened on top. Remove and leave to cool.

Combine all the ingredients in a blender with 185 ml (6 fl oz/¾ cup) water and blitz until smooth.

THE POWER OF A QUEST
by Andrew

A common thread that links many of the 'wellness warriors' in this chapter is the power behind their stories. We all know how it feels to struggle, and we all love watching people overcome adversity. The hero's journey always involves a mission, a purpose and an attempt to triumph against the odds – a quest, in other words. The people we admire have almost always found a way to do something that seems extremely difficult or impossible. People change their lives and indeed change the world by taking on extreme challenges and forging on until they are done. We are all capable of doing something big. We are all capable of taking on a challenge that will change our lives, whether it's running a marathon, learning an instrument, public speaking, starting a charity or eating potatoes! There's no way around it, extreme results require extreme action. An old football coach of mine used to say 'bite off more than you can chew and then chew like hell!'

JEANNINE ELDER
THE POTATO RESET

A lifetime of junk food ultimately led to health complications in Jeannine's early 30s: eczema, gallstones and severe hypothyroidism due to Hashimoto's disease. She switched to a plant-based diet in an effort to improve her health, but without much success at first, as she fell victim to the pull of vegan junk food (I can relate!).

She soon discovered the power of potatoes to heal the body and simplicity to heal the mind with her own month-long 'potato reset' in February of 2017. She proved, once again, that potatoes are the ultimate food, dropping 3.5 kg (8 lbs), beating cravings and changing her relationship with food in the process.

Since then, Jeannine has lost 15 kg (35 lb) eating a whole food, potato-based diet, and has inspired many others to do the same. She has helped many women with autoimmune conditions realise that they too can reach their healthy weight with the power of the potato.

BROCCOLI TOTS

I can't get enough of these! They are super easy to make, perfectly crisp on the outside and a great way to sneak in veggies. Veggie snobs and kids alike love these! Serves 1-2

60 g (2 oz/1 cup) broccoli florets
4 medium leftover baked potatoes
15 g (½ oz/¼ cup) nutritional yeast
1 teaspoon onion powder
½ teaspoon freshly ground black pepper

Separate broccoli into bite-sized pieces and remove the stems. Place the florets in a small saucepan of water and bring to gentle boil for 3 minutes. Drain, set aside and leave to cool.

While the broccoli is cooling, preheat the oven to 230°C (450°F). Line a baking tray with baking paper.

Grate the potatoes into a large mixing bowl. Finely chop the broccoli, then add to the potatoes with the rest of the ingredients. Stir until well combined.

Shape spoonfuls of the mixture into cylinder shapes (see Note) using your hands and place on the baking tray and repeat. Bake for 15 minutes, flip and bake for another 15–20 minutes, or until golden brown and crispy.

Note

Short on time? Roll into balls then flatten into patties instead of cylinders.

TIM KAUFMAN
FAT MAN RANTS

I have no hesitation in saying that Tim is one of the most inspiring people on the face of the planet. He was diagnosed with Ehlers-Danlos Syndrome (EDS) in his early twenties and was in chronic pain for most of his life. By the time he had reached the age of 37, he was addicted to Fentynal, alcohol and fast food. At over 180 kg (400 lb), he was unable to perform simple daily tasks. He had many chronic health issues and was almost immobile. He had lost his interest in life and had almost given up.

Soon after that, Tim started a journey to regain his health by changing one small thing at a time. He is now an athlete that thrives on a whole food, plant-based lifestyle and leads a healthy, happy, productive, and very active life free of all the medications he was once on. His passion is to spread the message that anyone can transition to a healthy, active lifestyle and dramatically change their life, regardless of their current situation or size.

I love Tim's sense of humour, his attitude to life and his willingness to go the extra mile for his own health and for anyone else who needs help, and I do mean anyone. When he's not running ultramarathons and ironman triathlons on knees and ankles that don't work properly, Tim spends his time talking to anyone who'll listen about just how drastically life can change if you 'eat plants and move your body. All ya gotta do is a little more than you did yesterday'.

FAT MAN'S GARLIC TATERS & GREENS

This is a staple food at my house. It takes minimal time to prepare and it's simple, cheap and so easy to make. I think it's the perfect mix of that 'comfort food' feeling with a powerhouse of nutrition provided by the greens. There are endless combinations for this dish as well. It works as a side dish or a standalone meal. I hope you enjoy it!
Serves 5 hungry people

Wash and quarter the potatoes (no need to peel) and place them in a large stockpot with the garlic cloves. Cover with cold water and bring to the boil over a high heat. Cook for 20 minutes, then drain and return to the pot with the remaining ingredients.

Blend with a hand-held blender until smooth and creamy. Serve over a heaping pile of mixed greens and top with some ground red pepper, if using.

2.25 kg (5 lb) red potatoes
10 garlic cloves
250 ml (8½ fl oz/1 cup) plant-based milk of your choice
2 teaspoons onion powder
3 teaspoons liquid aminos
30 g (1 oz/½ cup) nutritional yeast
420 g (15 oz) mixed greens, to serve
ground red pepper, to serve (optional)

ABOUT THE AUTHOR

Andrew Taylor's story went viral when the world caught wind of the then 36 year old Aussie dad who had embarked upon a quest to eat only potatoes for the entirety of 2016.

But to assume – as most did, at first – that this was some clown doing something crazy and unhealthy on a whim for 15 minutes of fame, was to miss both the perfect logic of the experiment itself, and the exceedingly powerful and timely message Andrew brings. Hint: it's not about the potatoes.

In late 2015, the former junior Australian Champion marathon kayaker was in the depths of despair after yet another failed attempt in a lifetime of dieting that had left him even heavier than before – 151.7kg.

From his black hole of clinical anxiety and depression, desperate to be the man he hoped his young son could look up to, he had an epiphany: he was a food addict.

Logically then, to Andrew, who thinks outside the square, he should treat his food addiction the same way you would treat any other addiction: through abstinence – or as close to it as you can get.

Armed with a degree in Applied Science and a fascination with all things nutrition-related, the high school teacher spent six weeks researching 'the perfect food' before he settled on the humble spud – just in time to begin a whole year break from thinking about food on New Year's Day, 2016.

With the media frenzy that followed his 'Spud Fit Challenge' story came the opportunity to help thousands of other food addicts deal with their own food psychology issues while losing weight and getting healthier along the way.

As a school teacher for the past seventeen years, Andrew has specialised in working with disadvantaged and at-risk youth. His passion for education and his ability to connect and communicate with the most vulnerable of students has been invaluable across his career. It is this experience that has given him the valuable insight and expertise that he has harnessed in his new role as health coach and motivator. Andrew has learned that, without exception, everyone wants to improve and is more than capable of making it happen for themselves. All they need to thrive is access to the right information and a supportive, encouraging environment.

'Spud Fit: a whole food potato-based guide to eating and living' represents Andrew's commitment to continued growth and learning. The appreciation and sharing of ground-breaking and life changing knowledge with the unique and awe-inspiring individuals he meets along the way has become his life's mission. There is beauty in simplicity, and the simple spud has proven itself to be the epitome of that.

Andrew is a motivational speaker and coach, who leads people through food addiction, weight loss and on to optimal health. His first short book, 'The D.I.Y. Spud Fit Challenge: a how-to guide to tackling food addiction with the humble spud' was co-authored by his wife Mandy van Zanen and has helped thousands of people to break the shackles of food addiction.

The 'Advanced DIY Spud Fit Challenge' is Andrew's online education program which takes members through an in depth, individually tailored approach to long term sustainable behaviour change. Through a series of 28 interactive lessons, members learn to tackle the root cause of their weight gain and ill health and apply simple, straightforward and logical steps to turning their life around.

Andrew is forever both grateful and amazed at what his life has become. It all started with a decision to stop waiting, wishing, hoping and dreaming and to start taking drastic action. Potatoes helped a little too!

Connect with Andrew at www.spudfit.com or as 'Spud Fit' on Facebook, Instagram, Youtube and Twitter.

ACKNOWLEDGEMENTS

None of this book would've happened without the incredible help and support of my wife, Mandy van Zanen. She routinely gets impossible things done and inspires me to do the same.

My big bloke, Teddy Taylor, was the catalyst for the complete overhaul of every aspect of my internal and external life. Thank you for showing me what's important.

My little bloke, Frank Taylor, is only 5 months old as I write this and his life so far has been hectic to say the least. With the benefit of hindsight we might've chosen a better time to make a book than during the first months of your life. Thank you for keeping a smile on your face and being so chilled out during such a crazy time.

Thank you to Talitha Case for our beautiful cover, and for generally creating and photographing genuine food art - a sentence never before uttered about pictures of potatoes!

Thank you to Noah Hannibal for doing some heavy lifting behind the lense for us late in the game. His powerful pictures added some much needed strength to this project.

Thank you to Liam Connole for his skill in managing to make my head look sufficiently different to the potatoes it was surrounded by in our photo shoot at Mitolo Group headquarters.

Thank you to Sarah Taylor for photos and for saving Mandy's sanity on more than one occasion.

Thank you to our team of proofreaders: Amanda, Kate, Michelle, Amanda, Jan - EPIC job, thank you SO much!

Thank you to Cindy for loaning us her kitchen to cook and photograph. If we had attempted this in our own kitchen we would've been crushed under an avalanche of spuds!

Thank you to Angela Dressel, designer, for helping a random fellow local with InDesign and thus putting an end to the nuclear meltdown that was happening in Mandy's brain. We've both been through enough steep learning curves for one year!

Special thank you to our parents, for all the babysitting and for your moral support and encouragement.

Also to Josie, Zoe, Amanda and Jonesy - all busy mothers themselves - who used up their own precious 'me' time to come to Mandy's rescue (we owe you!). There's no way this could have happened without any of you. We'll get back to being parents now so you can all recover in time for the next book!

Xybil Respicio has worked tirelessly alongside us on putting this together and doing a lot of the stuff that would explode my tiny brain. Thank you for your patience in dealing with endless edits and changes and indulging our perfectionist tendencies.

Thank you to all 93 (!) of our amazing contributors! When we first hatched the idea for this book we thought it would be a fun little project and it would be cool to get some other people involved. We truly have been blown away by everyone's willingness to be involved and help us put this together. This project quickly became much bigger and better than we ever could've imagined, thank you all for your creativity, generosity and patience.

There are so many more people who deserve to be thanked on the pages of this book but it has to end somewhere! Thank you to everyone who has supported us in this strange and wonderful new life we lead. Being a writer and entrepreneur (I use those words lightly!) is so much harder than we ever imagined it would be. The support and love from our friends, family and supporters from all over the world is what keeps us going.

CONTRIBUTOR DIRECTORY

ADAM GUTHRIE (The I Feel Good Program)
Rainbow Jungle Curry, page 144
Web: ifeelgood.com.au
    ifeelgoodmag
    ifeelgoodmagazine

ADAM SUD
Purple Sweet Potato Cinnamon Oatmeal, page 218
Web: masteringdiabetes.org
Web: engine2diet.com
    plantbasedaddict
    @plantbasedaddict

AMANDA MEGGISON
Potato and Tomato Curry & Gnocchi with a Basic Tomato Sauce, page 101-104
Web: plantedlife.com.au
    plantedlifeau
    @plantedlifeau
    @plantedlifeau

AMANDA RAE
Potato and Mushroom Stew, page 146
Web: Groundleaf.co
    groundleaf
    @groundleaf
    Ground Leaf

AMANDA ROSE
Mexican Smokey Loaded Fries, page 92
Web: becomeaplantbasedbabe.com
    amandaroseofficial
    @amandaroseofficial
    @plantbasedbabes
    Amanda Rose

AMRITA - CRAZY VEGAN KITCHEN
No Oil Herb and Mustard Potato Salad, page 148
Web: crazyvegankitchen.com
    crazyvegankitchen
    @crazyvegankitchen
    @crazyvegankitch

ANDREW'S MUM (Kate Taylor)
Spuds with asparagus & edamame, page 16

ANIMAL LIBERATION AUSTRALIA
Sweet Potato and Kale Chilli, page 162
Web: alv.org.au
    animalliberationvictoria
    @animallib

VEGAN EASY
Potato Tornados, page 176
Web: veganeasy.org
    veganeasy
    @veganeasy

ANIMALS AUSTRALIA
Hearty Corn and Potato Chowder, page 160
Web: animalsaustralia.org
    AnimalsAustralia
    @AnimalsAus
    Animals Australia

ANJA CASS (Cooking with plants)
Mediterranean Style Potato Salad, page 150
Web: Cookingwithplants.com
    Cookingwithplants
    @CookWithPlants
    CookingWithPlants

ANTHONY DISSEN MA, RDN
Portuguese Caldo Verde, page 60
Web: AnthonyDissen.com
    NaturalRD
    @anthonydissenrd

ANTHONY MASIELLO
Chickpea Potato Curry with Kale, page 220
Web: Healthyhumanrevolution.com
Email: anthony@healthyhumanrevolution.com
    anthonymasiello
    @amasiello

BEN AND LOUISE LOAKER
Crunchy Curried Potatoes, page 222
    Whole food Whole Health

CARYN DUGAN
Sushi, page 152
Web: stlveggirl.com
    stlveggirl
    @stlveggirl
    @stlveggirl

CATHY FISHER
Beefless Stew, page 153
Website StraightUpFood.com
    StraightUpFood
    StraightUpFood
    StraightUpFood

CHEF AJ
The McDougall/Goldhamer cauliflower risotto sweet potato stack stack, Sweet potato mousse with caramelised apples, Cauliflower Bisque, page 118-120

Web: Chefajwebsite.com
    chef.aj1
    therealchefaj
    CHEF AJ

CHEF DEL SROUFE
Spicy Thai 'Meatballs' with Orange Chili Dipping Sauce, page 122
Web: chefdelsroufe.com
    ChefDelSroufe
    @chefdelsroufe
    @delmasg

CHEF NA
Tom Yum, page 124
Website chefna.com.au

CHEF RAMSES BRAVO
Baked Yams with Corn Chow Chow, page 126
Web: cheframses.com
    Bravo Cookbook

CHERIE TU
Chili Stuffed Potatoes, page 224
Website cherietu.com
- @thrivingonplants
- thrivingonplants

CLARE MANN
Roast Potato Scramble with Gherkins and Red Pepper, page 168
Web: veganpsychologist.com
      vystopia.com
      claremann.com

DR CONOR KERLEY
Potato and Leek Soup, page 82
Email: conorkerleynutrition@gmail.com
- conor.kerley
- @conorkerley
- @conorkerley

CORINNE NIJJER
Rainbow Baked Potatoes, page 203-204
Web: corinnenijjer.com
- corinne.nijjer
- @corinnenijjer
- @CorinneNijjer
- Corinne Nijjer

CRISSI CARVALHO
German Kartoffel Potato Muscle Pancakes, page 94
Web: veganfitnessmodel.com
Email: info@veganfitnessmodel.com
- crissicarvalho
- @veganfitnessmodel
- Vegan Fitness Model

CYRUS AND ROBBY (Mastering Diabetes)
Sweet Potatoes Loaded with Lentil Stew, page 84
Web: masteringdiabetes.org
- masteringdiabetes.org
- masteringdiabetes
- mindfuldiabeticrobby
- mangomannutrition

DEREK SIMNETT
Miso Baked Potatoes with Peas, page 62
- simnettnutrition
- simnettnutrition
- Signet Nutrition

DR ASH NAYATE
Breakfast potatoes, page 166
Web: www.ashnayate.com

DOCTORS FOR NUTRITION (Lucy Stegley)
Cauli Potato Mash with Mushroom Macadamia Gravy, page 44
Web: doctorsfornutrition.org

DR ANTHONY HADJ
Dr Anthony's Cheesy Hummus Potato Bake, page 24
Web: livelongertoday.com

DR ARMANDO GONZALES
Dr Mondo's Loaded 'Carnitas' Papas, page 26
Web: drmondo.org

DR DOUG LISLE
The Pleasure Trap, page 86
Web: esteemdynamics.org/

DR GARTH DAVIS
Baked Sweet Potates with Black Beans, Pico, Spinach, Avocado and Sriracha, page 28
Web: proteinaholic.com
- drgarth
- @drgarthdavis

DR IRMINNE VAN DYKEN
Russell's Turmeric Infused Super Duper Antioxidant 'Cheese' Sauce, page 30
Web: outofthedoldrums.com
- Out of the Doldrums
- out_of_the_doldrums
- Out of the Doldrums

DR JOEL KAHN
Loaded Sweet Potato, page 32
Web: drjoelkahn.com

DR JOHN MCDOUGALL
Crock Pot Potatoes, page 20
Web: drmcdougall.com
- DrJohnMcDougall
- @johnmcdougallmd

DR LAURIE MARBAS
Sweet Potato Red Lentil Stew, page 34
- lmarbas
- @lauriemarbas

DR LUKE WILSON
Simple Pumpkin and Potato Soup, page 36
Web: twozestybananas.com
- twozestybananas
- twozestybananas

DR MALCOLM MACKAY & JENNY CAMERON
Spuds on the go, page 48
Website drmalcolmmackay.com.au
        wholefoodsplantbasedhealth.com.au
- PlantBasedHealthAustralia

DR MICHAEL GREGER
Stuffed Sweet Potatoes With Balsamic-date Glaze, page 46
Web: nutritionfacts.org
- NutritionFacts.org
- @nutrition_facts_org
- @nutrition_facts
- NutritionFactsOrg

DR MICHAEL KLAPER
Ave Spud, page 38
Web: doctorklaper.com
- michaelklapermd
- @michaelklapermd

DR MONICA AGGARWAL
Sweet Potato Humus, page 40
Web: Drmonicaaggarwal.com
- @strongheartdoc

DR NEAL BARNARD
Mashed Potatoes, page 22
☐   NealBarnardMD

DR RENAE THOMAS
Chocolate Cake, page 42
Web   livefull.com.au
email   renae@livefull.com.au
☐   @drrenaethomas

EMILY HAZELL (Serotonin Eatery)
Serotonin Spud, page 128
Web: serotonindealer.com
☐   serotonindealer
☐   @serotonindealer

EMMA MOIGNARD (Soulful Vegan Food)
Macaroni and Cheese, page 130
☐   soulfulveganfood
☐   soulfulveganfood

EMMA ROCHE (Plant Plate)
Potato and Broccoli Dal, Crispy Baked Potato Hash with Homemade Salsa, page 132-133
Web: plantplate.com
☐   plantplate
☐   @plantplate

GEORGIE MANKEY (Fit with Georgie)
Vegan Cheesy Pasta Sauce Two Ways, page 208-209
☐   FitWithGeorgie
☐   @fitwithgeorgie
☐   Fit With Georgie

ANJI BEE (Happy Healthy Vegan)
Green Bean and Potato Subji, page 164
Web: happyhealthyvegan.org
☐   happyhealthyvegan
☐   @happyhealthyvegan
☐   @Anji Bee
☐   @happyhealthyvegan

HANNAH JANISH (High Carb Hannah)
Broccoli Cheddar Soup, page 184
Web: rawtillwhenever.com

HOWARD JACOBSON (Plant yourself)
Recipe for Appreciating the humble spuds, page 54
Web: WellStartHealth.com
         PlantYourself.com

IIDA VAN DER BYL-KNOEFEL (A kitchen fairytale)
Finnish Summer Soup, page 136
☐   @akitchenfairytale

JACKSON FOSTER (Plantriotic)
Sweet Potato Banana Smoothie, page 226
☐   @plantriotic

JAMES ASPEY
Cinnamon-spiced sweet potato pancakes, page 180
☐   jamesaspeyactivism
☐   @jamesaspey
☐   James & Carly

JEANNINE ELDER (Potato Wisdom)
Broccoli Tots, page 228
Web: potatoreset.com
☐   potatowise
☐   @potato.wisdom
☐   potatowisdom

JOEL KIRKILIS
Potato Salad, page 98
☐   @joel_kirks

JOSH LAJAUNIE
Deconstructed Potato Salad, page 186
Web: joshlajaunie.com
☐   joshla.juanie
☐   @joshlajuanie
☐   @joshlajuanie

KATHY ASHTON
Crunchy Potato Balls, page 64
Web: flourishln.com.au

CHEF KATIE MAE (The Culinary Gym)
Spicy Sweet Potato Hash, page 138
Web: theculinarygym.com
         theculinarygym
         @theculinarygym
         The Culinary Gym

KLAUS MITCHELL (Plant Based News)
Potato Shashlik, page 174
Web: plantbasednews.org
☐   plantbasednews
☐   @plantbasednews
☐   @plantbasednews
☐   plantbasednews

LUKE AND EMILIE TAN (Plant fit movement)
Indian Shepherds' Pie, page 100
Web: awakemethod.com
☐   Live Green Live Lean
☐   @livegreenlivelean
☐   @emilieendurancerunner

MANDY VAN ZANEN
Spud Fit recipes, Chapter 1
Web: mandyvanzanen.com
☐   mvanzanen
☐   mandyvanzanen
☐   mandyvanzanen

MATT GRILLS
The Froth is High Salad, page 114
Web: thetattoorunner.com
☐   TattooRunner
☐   Adventures and Activism

JAIME AND SIMON (Messy Veggies)
Garlic and thyme sweet potatoes with vegan parmesan, page 190
Web: messyveggies.com
☐   messyveggies.com
☐   @messy.veggies

TONI OKAMOTO & MICHELLE CEHN

Sweet Potato Toast, page 142

Web: worldofvegan.com

           Plantbasedonabudget.com

TRINA STEELE

Lentil Spiced Pie, page 206

      trinasteele

VICTORIA LISSACK

Super Easy Sweet Potato Smoothie Bowl, page 112

Web: victorialissack.com

      @victoria_lissack

      Victoria Lissack

      VictoriaLissack

VICTORIA MORAN (Main Street Vegan)

Yogi's Yellow Potato Curry, page 170

Web: mainstreetvegan.net

WILL KRISKI

Shredded Hash Brown Omelette, page 216

Web: potatostrong.com

      PotatoStrong

      @potatostrong

PHOTO/PUBLISHER CREDITS

SPUD fit PHOTOS

COVER PHOTO: Talitha Case (page 139)

Also pages III, 27, 31, 33, 37, 39, 71, 89, 95, 97 (food), 105, 117, 119, 177, 207
 Noah Hannibal - page 10, 231, 233,
 Liam Connole - page VI, X, XII, XIV
Bree Gaudette - page V
Sarah Taylor - page 61, 99
Chloe Angelo - page 104

All photos contributors' own, except:

ANIMALS AUSTRALIA, Recipe & Styling: Deb Kaloper - https://www.instagram.com/debkaloper/

Photography: Chris Middleton - http://chrismiddletonphoto.com/

Food prep: Caroline Griffiths - https://www.instagram.com/carolines_food_stuff/

ALV AND VEGAN EASY, photo by alv.org.au

ADAM SUD, Photo by Amy Harris (Amy Loo Photography)

AMANDA ROSE, Photo by Angel Riley photography

ANTHONY MASIELLO, Photo by Jason Cohen.

BEN LOAKER, Photo by Tim Loft

CATHY fiSHER, Food by Cathy Fisher, photo of Cathy by Cathy Stancil.

CLINT AND MELISSA PADDISON, Photo by Jazzy Photography

DR ASH NAYATE, Personal photo by Australian Vegan Journal and Vegan Kids Magazine

DR IRMINNE VAN DYKEN, Photo by Barbara's camera

DR JOHN MCDOUGALL, Photo by Emma Roche.

DR LUKE WILSON, Photo by Tamara Josephine Photography

DR NEAL BARNARD, Photo from Alyssa Luning.

DR MICHAEL GREGER:

From HOW NOT TO DIE: DISCOVER THE FOODS SCIENTIFICALLY PROVEN TO PREVENT AND REVERSE DISEASE © 2015 by Michael Greger. Reprinted by permission of Flat Iron Books. All Rights Reserved.

Recipe Photo by Antonis Achilleos.

EMMA ROCHE, Originally published in 'Whole Food Plant Based on $5 a Day'.

HOWARD JACOBSON, Photos by Yael Zivan.

ANJI BEE, HAPPY HEALTHY VEGAN, This recipe is included in the 'Keep It Carbed, Baby!' cookbook by Anji Bee, released in 2016.

MICHELE MARTINEZ, Profile Photo by Stoney Photography.

NICOLETTE RICHER, Photo by Jessie McNaught.

NINA AND RANDA NELSON, Reprinted with permission from the publisher, Hachette Book Group. Portrait Photo by Brad Buckman. Photo by Char Nolan.

SETAREH KHATIBI, Photo by Dominick Aznavour.

TIMAREE HAGENBURGER, Recipe photo by Scot Hagenburger (my husband) and Profile photo by Kathryn Mayo.

NATASHA AND LUCA, THAT VEGAN COUPLE, This recipe is included in the 'Recipes For Healthy Vegan Eating' ebook by Natasha & Luca, released in 2016.

JACKSON FOSTER, PLANTRIONIC, Photo by Tyler Marshall.

PETER SINGER, Photo by Alletta Vaandering.

CPSIA information can be obtained
at www.ICGtesting.com
Printed in the USA
BVHW021553170621
609826BV00011B/2086

9 780995 409613